ADA C

D1457461

Dear Folks,

STEVEN DAVIS

This book is dedicated to the doughboys and women of WWI who left the safety of home to aid the war effort with heart and soul. They placed love of country and family above all else. It is also dedicated to the parents and loved ones who had the courage to let them go.

Greet them ever with grateful hearts.

To the Reader

Earl Young was born on May 2, 1899, in Brock, Nebraska, and enlisted in the army in 1918. Earl Young is my grandfather. He was a soldier in the A.E.F., the American Expeditionary Force, which was dispatched to France during World War I. A few years ago, while sorting some of my grandparents' belongings, I made a discovery. I opened a suitcase that had been long forgotten and found hundreds of family photographs, memorabilia, and an old two-pound box of chocolates. The chocolates were long gone but the box was an excellent container that stored and preserved letters Earl had written while in the army. Some letters had been kept in their original envelopes and some were loose, many dated in 1918 and 1919.

Earl mailed letters and postcards to his mother and father in Brock, Nebraska, and to his brother, George, in Dalton, Nebraska, as well as to other brothers and sisters. Some letters were written in ink and easy to read, while others were difficult, as they were written on thin paper, front and back, and in pencil. Some were written using a canteen or his knee for a desk. The light wasn't always adequate as some were written by candlelight. Each letter was handled multiple times by family and friends and sometimes mailed again to other relatives, which was common in those days.

While reading the letters, I saw a story that deserved to be told, and I knew then and there I wanted to write an historical fiction book, using the accounts in the letters. *Dear Folks* displays a number of copies of the actual letters and envelopes, but there is a transcription for every letter. These transcriptions are just as Earl wrote each letter—with no correction of spelling, grammar, or punctuation. I have used episodes in Earl's life and memories of experiences shared with my grandfather and family history to create the story contained in this book. Family photographs and other items Earl brought home are in the book as well. Sheet music, circa 1918, that relates to Earl's letters is interspersed throughout. With the letters as a guide, this book is based on actual events and the people in Earl's life. This is his story.

Camp A. A. Humphrey
5th E. T. R.,
Virginia.

Dear Folks,

I just received your long
waited for letter a few moments
ago and sure can say that I am
proud of the button I wear now
days, possibly a little prouder than
any body in camp.

I suppose you wish most to
know just what every body is doing
here. In one word we are all doing
the same thing at the same time.

A good many of us enlisted men
have been transfered from the work
we thought we were to get into.

I enlisted in the Quarter Master
Corpse, and here I am in the Engineers
Corpse. (This last word sounds bad but it is
pronounced thus — "Core".)

1

Proud of the Buttons

Camp A. A. Humphrey
5th E. T. R.
Virginia
August 11, 1918

Dear Folks,

    I just received your long wanted for letter a few moments ago and sure can say that I am proud of the buttons I wear now days, possibly a little prouder than anybody in camp.

    I suppose you wish most to know just what everybody is doing here. In one word we are all doing the same thing at the same time. A good many of us enlisted men have been transferred from the work we thought we were to get into. I enlisted in the quarter Master Corpse and here I am in the Engineer Corpse. (This last word sounds bad but it is pronounced thus—"core").

    At this particular camp they started us out last week at Pontoon bridge building. A Pontoon is a boat about 25 feet long & 4 feet wide, run by 4 or 6 propellers, of course by man power, you know. To build the bridge the men are all lined up on shore divided into a dozen squads or so of about 6 to 20

men to each squad according to the work assignment by the
Lieutenant. We are told what to do.

First a bunch get the boatsman on the first part started,
second the boat crews get their boats lined out, headed up
stream one beside the other about 20 feet apart clear across the
river to be bridged. Then the stringers are carried out, then the
planks. Special men for each job. I & 8 others had the job of
tying these stringers to the boats, each boat is anchored good.
We built a bridge & tore it down every morning last week. Also
we broke all records for building and tearing down a 240 ft.
bridge. The old records were done in 36 ½ minutes. We did it
in 31 minutes.

Our captains are with us when it comes to telling the
public about it. Really something to be proud of. Not a nail
used in the bridge. We also had lessons on how to row a boat
correctly. I am no so proud of our afternoon work. Each afternoon except Saturday we had a pick, shovel & a wheelbarrow
making roads for this camp. This camp was just started last
January here in the middle of a wilderness in the hills like
the Schafer hill. Once in a while there is a patch kinda level
though. These places have been and will be grubbed and leveled off for drill grounds in the near future.

Believe me it is hot here, the hottest hole I ever witnessed,
and not stretching it any either. The sweat just runs down your
nose and ozzes out through the uniform all over. We take our
time when it comes to pitching dirt.

When we get in evenings the sun is way up yet. Then we
stand retreat, get in line for supper and then the sun is still up
yet 2 rods or so. Lots of time for baseball, shower baths and
everything. No one is tired when the work is all done . . .

• • •

Earl paused writing the letter and looked out the window of the barracks to gather his thoughts. He shook his head in disbelief at the hot, steamy woods of his new living quarters. Summer in Virginia. He thought he must be dreaming he was at a Virginia army training base. Life had gone by as fast as a lightning bolt in a thunderstorm on the plains since turning the age of eighteen on May 2, 1918. It was just a few days ago he'd made the decision to join the Army Expeditionary Force and say goodbye to life as he knew it in Nebraska. He wiped his forehead with his sleeve, wondering how you could work up a sweat just writing a letter. He started to write again when his thoughts were interrupted.

"Hey Earl—daydreaming about Nebraska again? How about some dominoes?" said Morgan, the soldier who slept in the bunk below Earl. Earl was taller, so he had been assigned the top bunk.

"Want to put down that pen and give me a chance to best you in some dominoes?" asked Morgan. He raised himself up on one elbow, ready to set up a game if Earl agreed.

"Yes sir. A game of dominoes is just what I need to cheer me up and try to forget what a hot, miserable day it is out there today," said Earl. He turned around in his chair to face Morgan and wiggled his ears up and down. Up and down.

Morgan laughed. "How in the world do you do that? Since these nineteen days I've known you, it always cheers me up. I've lived in Michigan my entire life and never saw anyone who could wiggle *just* their ears."

Earl just wiggled them some more and didn't say a word. Morgan smiled widely and said, "It really does make me laugh until my sides hurt. But I still want you to play some dominoes."

"Give me a few minutes to finish my letter. I've got to get this posted in case I don't get a chance in the next few days. The only reason I'm in the army is my folks gave their permission as long as

I promised to write as often as I could and let them know where I was," explained Earl.

Morgan lay back on his pillow, not happy he had to wait for a domino game. He had promised to write home too but somehow always found something else to occupy his time. He thought about polishing his boots but it seemed too hot to do anything unless ordered to do so.

Earl rubbed his arm and picked up his pen to finish writing the letter . . .

• • •

There is always something going on in the Y.M.C.A. of the evening. The piano and about 100 male voices singing "Keep the Home Fires Burning" here right now. One don't realize the meaning of these songs until he gets 2,500 miles from home & friends. A vaudeville here immediately, no charge here in the "Y" as it is called. They furnish all of the writing paper, envelopes, ink & pens here.

I have such a cold I can hardly breath now but it is losing all up now. We are vaccinated for Smallpox & Typhoid fever here so there is hardly a chance of getting cooped, or rather, sick.

I can't get anything here for less than 3 prices for anything and maybe not then. I had my first day of drill yesterday. My right arm & shoulder is so sore today I can hardly handle the pick & shovel today. I expect gun drill again on Wednesday.

A letter cheers the most. Will get the regulations on color of sweater.
Earl
Lots more news but not this time.

• • •

Earl signed his name and folded the letter. Thank goodness the army furnished all the writing materials he needed to keep his family informed. His mother insisted he try to write whenever he could. He couldn't figure out why she worried so much about him. He did enjoy writing so he could tell his family about his experiences and he knew if he wrote letters, he could expect to receive some back. It certainly cheered him up whenever he received one. As he put the letter in an envelope, he hummed the words to one of the favorite songs at the Y—it was called "Keep the Home Fires Burning."

"Keep the Home-Fires Burning (Till the Boys Come Home)"
Song lyrics by Lena Guilbert Ford, music by Ivor Novello, 1915

They were summoned from the hillside;
They were called in from the glen,
And the Country found them ready
At the stirring call for men.

Let no tears add to their hardship,
As the Soldiers pass along,
And although your heart is breaking,
Make it sing this cheery song.

Keep the Home-Fires burning,
While your hearts are yearning.
Though your lads are far away,
They dream of Home;
There's a silver lining
Through the dark cloud shining.
Turn the dark cloud inside out,
Till the boys come Home.

Overseas there came a pleading,
"Help a nation in distress!"
And we gave our glorious laddies,
Honour bade us do no less.

For no gallant Son of freedom
To a tyrant's yoke should bend,
And a noble heart must answer
To the sacred call of "Friend."

Earl reflected on the day, took a deep breath, and looked out the window again. He could see the Virginia trees suffering under the heat of the day and pictured his mother at her kitchen table, looking out the window at the trees on their farm, barely breathing, waiting for the next letter to arrive saying where he was and that he was okay. If truth be known, letter writing helped him as much as it helped his family. It eased his loneliness, somehow, like he was talking to his parents or brothers or sisters but instead writing down his thoughts in the form of a letter. Until joining the army, he'd never been out of the state of Nebraska. Now he was in Virginia, about as far away from his home state as he could be and still be in the U.S.A.

· · ·

On August 6, the enlisted men at Fort Logan, Colorado, had been in formation at 3:15 p.m. and were told to gather their packs and be ready to board a train to Virginia by 3:45. Earl had been expecting a move with little time to pack, so it didn't take him long.

He had been in the army just a month, a private—and privates were the last to know anything until the moment it happened. Earl mailed the postcard in Rulo, Nebraska, the last stop before crossing over the Missouri River. Mailing the postcard was symbolic. It was a last goodbye before the arduous work ahead to help defeat the Kaiser.

The beautiful golden wheat fields in Dalton, Nebraska, that he had helped George harvest just a month ago were on his mind. He thought of his mother in her vegetable garden in Brock, caring for her prized tomatoes. He thought about both of his parents and knew they would be worried about him. Earl wished they had received his telegram so he could have waved to them when the train crossed over the Missouri river on his way to Camp Humphreys. Even though he knew his parents were very concerned for his safety, Earl felt strong and unwavering in his decision to join the U.S. Army. He felt optimistic that things would work out. What could go wrong? Anyway, it was time to say goodbye to Nebraska. He hoped he would soon be saying hello to France. It was time for him to be a soldier.

"It's Time for Every Boy to Be a Soldier"
Song lyrics by Alfred Bryan,
music by Harry Tierney, 1917

Most ev'ry fellow has a sweetheart,
Some little girl with eyes of blue.
My Daddy also had a sweetheart,
And he fought to win her too.
There'll come a day when we must pay
The price of love and duty.
Be there staunch and true.

It's time for ev'ry boy to be a soldier,
To put his strength and courage to the test.
It's time to place a musket on his shoulder,
And wrap the Stars and Stripes around his breast.
It's time to shout those noble words of Lincoln,
And stand up for the land that gave you birth.
'That the nation of the people, by the people, for the people,
Shall not perish from the earth.'

Boys of America, get ready,
Your motherland is calling you.
Boys of America, be steady,
For the Old Red, White, and Blue.
When Yankee Doodle comes to town
Upon his little pony,
Be there staunch and true.

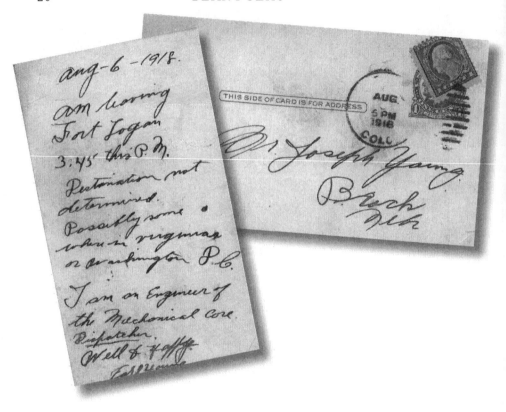

Mr. Joseph Young
Brock, Nebr.
August 6, 1918

> *Am leaving Fort Logan 3:45 this p.m.*
> *Destination not determined.*
> *Possibly somewhere in Virginia or Washington D.C.*
> *I am an Engineer of the Mechanical Core Dispatcher.*

Well & Happy.
Earl Young

Earl was glad to get that quick postcard off to his father, Joseph, before leaving Fort Logan. And while on the train headed to Virginia, he dashed off another quick postcard to his brother, George.

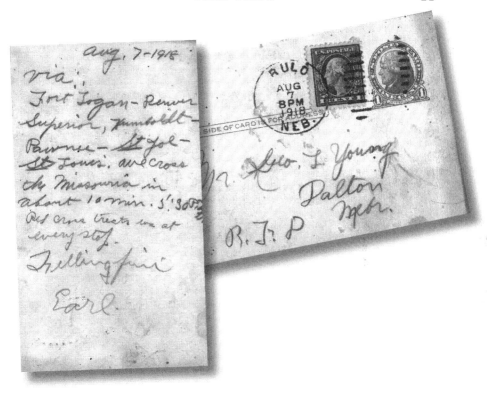

Mr. George L. Young
Dalton, Nebr.
R.F.D.
August 7, 1918

    Via: Fort Logan – Denver, Superior, Humboldt – Pawnee
– St. Joe – St. Louis. We cross the Missouria in about 10
minutes. 5:30 p.m. Red Cross treats us at every stop.
Feeling fine.
Earl

ST. LOUIS, MO
AUG 8
5:30 PM
1918

Mr. Joseph Young.

Brock,

Nebr.

St Louis, Mo
Aug 8-1918.

Dear Folks.

I hardly know who to
address these cards & letters to but
I want you all to put in a
word or two frequently just the
same.

I haven't had a real decent chance
to write a letter since night before
last. We started from Denver, just two
coaches of us, on the Burlington, came
through Humboldt yesterday at about
5 P.M. I sure looked every direction
for you, but concluded that you surely
didn't get my telegram in time to
come down. Oh well it is just a
short little trip for you to come & see me
even if I do go to the atlantic coast for
training?

We crossed the Missouria at Rulo last evening.
St. Louis, MO
August 8, 1918

Dear Folks,
*   I hardly know who to address these cards & letters to but I*
want you all to put in a word or two frequently just the same.
*   I haven't had a real decent chance to write a letter since*
night before last. We started from Denver, just two coaches of
us, on the Burlington, came through Humboldt yesterday at
about 5 p.m. I sure looked every direction for you, but con-
cluded that you surely didn't get my telegram in time to come
down. Oh well it is just a short little trip for you to come & see
me even if I do go to the Atlantic coast for training?
*   I sure am having a time of my life. Seeing everything from*
the snowy peaks on the Rockie Mountains to a steam ship – a
real one – for the first time this morning. We have slept two
nights in Pullmans with real beds.
*   It sure surprised me to be woke up this morning by the*
chug-chug of the old steamboat going up stream about as fast
as we were going down. It was about 250 feet long. Dozens of
the smaller ones down here by town. I am turned around here
in this berg. The first time in my life.
*   The Red Cross girls just keep a fellow stuffed with candy,*
ice cream, punch, good water & lots of cigarettes and best of
all, I helped wear out sixteen, more or less, pianos in the last
week. Everybody shaking hands, waving, hollering, saying
goodby all the way along. Down at St. Joseph last night a
dozen girls, Red Cross of course, stood amongest us at the cars
waiting till time to leave, singing all the songs that we ever
heard. Of course, the boys were singing too.
*   I almost broke my neck last night when we were all turned*
loose in the swimming pool. I was learning to dive, jumped
in head first and struck the bottom with the top of my head.
It's (my neck of course) so stiff this morning that I can hardly

turn it. The top of my head is so sore I can hardly run a comb though my hair without hollering. There is so much music going on now that I can't think of anything much to write. Candy box just passed again and here comes the figgs.

I passed a month one physical examination at Fort Logan. Just 71 ½" tall, weigh 141 lbs., 6" chest expansion, 3 degree arch in feet. The best that anyone ever has. 20/20 eyes, teeth, nose, throat and ears which means as good as anybodys a going.

Lot of the fellows fainted when they were "shot in the arm" for typhoid fever, but it never fazed me a bit. After we passed all the examinations they marched us down to the Insurance office & explained that to us. There wasn't one that didn't take $10,000 insurance and signed it to Mother. If we just get crippled we get the $50 a month. If killed it will be paid the same way to you. It just takes the place with the old way of the pension. So, you see, whatever comes up, there won't be any cowards knowing that the ones at home will be cared for, while if crippled we ourselves won't need to sell shoe strings on the corner for a living.

It sure is awfully hot down here in these old valleys. The Mountains for mine. (More candy.) (Butter scotch & wafers.) (Mum. Mmmmmmmm.) We are promised a ride through this berg, by the Red Cross kids. They sure make a hit with the boys and make us happy & forget the unpleasant things that frequently comes up.

We are blessed with a good natured Corporal & Sargent. We leave here for somewhere. I don't know & don't care where to at 8:20 p.m.

Good By,
Earl
(Support the Red Cross with all your might. And don't forget).

Earl's suitcase collection

WHEN you reach camp you will be definitely assigned to quarters. Within a few days you will receive the regulation uniform and equipment. After this there will be no need for civilian clothing and it would be well to return it at once to the folks at home by parcel post. The Y. M. C. A. Secretaries at the hut nearest to your quarters will be glad to furnish wrapping material for this purpose.

While in camp in this country you may write as many letters as you desire. As soon as you find out what your permanent regiment and company address will be, forward it to those from whom you expect to receive mail so they may know how to address mail to reach you promptly.

The Young Men's Christian Association, the Young Men's Hebrew Association, the Knights of Columbus, and similar organizations, furnish free all the writing paper and envelopes that you may want. You will also find writing desks, pens, ink and pencils furnished without expense to you and your only cost will be postage. There is no limit to the number of letters you may receive.

When you get over-seas, all the writing paper, envelopes and post-cards you want will be furnished to you free by the Y. M. C. A. and these other organizations.

Every man in the service of the United States Army or Navy is entitled to a maximum of $10,000 insurance. Less than this can be taken if desired but it is urged that every man who can possibly do so take this $10,000 insurance. It can be secured at a very nominal cost per month for which arrangements can be made to have the premium deducted from the monthly pay. It affords the best protection for yourself provided you should be permanently disabled while in the service, and also affords protection for your dependents. As soon as you are assigned to a company with a permanent officer in command, get from him the cost for the insurance and the method to be followed in securing same.

In most camps provision is made for the proper entertainment and care of visitors. The Young Women's Christian Association provides in many of the larger camps in this country Hostess Houses where work in cooperation with the Young Men's Christian Association is done and where your mother, sister, wife or sweetheart may visit you. If you intend to have anyone visit you at camp, it would be well for you to take the matter up with the Red Triangle Secretary located nearest you and get his advice and counsel.

At every camp at home and abroad you will find Red Triangle (Y. M. C. A.) buildings and Secretaries. Your uniform is your membership ticket. They furnish, free, entertainments, religious services, writing material, etc., and help in every way they can to make life at camp just as pleasant as possible. Y. M. C. A. Secretaries go with you every step of the way from the time you leave home until you return at the close of the War.

Wherever you may be, remember that whenever you see the Red Triangle or the letters "Y. M. C. A.," they signify to you a cordial welcome and as you leave they flash forth this message, "You Must Come Again."

At some Y. M. C. A.'s outside the camps, a nominal charge is made for some of the privileges, such as beds, but it is as low as possible consistent with first-class service.

Over-seas the Y. M. C. A. carries on all the work that it does at home and serves the men in many additional ways.

WHY WE FIGHT

We fight because we could not avoid war and preserve national honor.

We fight because an arrogant power challenged our freedom on the sea and, without warning and without reason, sank vessels carrying American men, women and children across the open highway of the ocean.

We fight to save for those we love the priceless boon of liberty for which our fathers fought in days long past.

We fight to keep unpolluted and holy the American home.

We fight to make this old world worth living in for those dear to us and for those who are to follow after our day is spent.

We fight to protest to the death against barbarism and cruelty such as have prevailed and are prevailing in the conquered territories of Belgium, France, Russia, Armenia and the Balkan States.

We fight to protect the just rights of weaker nations against the iron and unscrupulous might of the strong and the powerful.

We fight for the sake of outraged women of many lands; for helpless children stricken down in sacred youth; for men maimed and slaughtered beneath the juggernaut of Imperial ambition; for the old and the young of those hapless nations crushed by Teutonic ruthlessness. We fight because we cannot endure such things and not fight and still retain character and manhood.

We fight because our enemies seek to despoil and destroy the sacred land of our heritage; to bind free-born Americans in fetters of serfdom and to drag us captive in the train of their triumphant procession.

We fight without hunger for indemnity and without unholy longing for territory; anxious only to bear our share of the heavy burden of saving civilization from the blight of so-called "kultur."

We fight because God has called us and we have heard His call summoning men of every nation and creed to serve Him in this, the testing day of nations.

For reasons unselfish and exalted, our country has entered this war to remain in it until her victorious sons return with her flag bathed in new glory. We must and we shall win because the courage of a just cause masters our souls; because our nation in this day appraises righteousness more than comfort and because a free people prefer death to slavery.

"Who are you writing to anyway?" asked Morgan. His face had a wide grin as he asked, "Your girl back in ole Nebraska?"

"No, I don't have a girlfriend back in Nebraska or anywhere else," said Earl.

"Are you sure?" Morgan pressed his point. "You spend so much time writing letters or postcards I don't know when you find time to build a bridge or clean your rifle. There must be a girl."

Earl looked earnestly at Morgan and said, "Well . . ."

"You can tell me Earl. I won't tell anyone," Morgan said as he crossed his heart.

Earl looked up at the ceiling, collecting his thoughts. "Okay, Morgan," he said. "Actually there are two girls."

"Two! Two girls?"

"That's right," said Earl. "Two. And not only that, they're twins."

"Twins? You've got two girls? And they're twins?" Morgan said with excitement all over his face. "Tell me more!"

"Well, what else do you want to know?" asked Earl with cooperation in his voice and a twinkling in his eyes.

"Okay. What are their names?" Morgan asked.

"Millie and Mabel."

"How did you meet them?"

"Well, I was introduced to them when I came home from the hospital."

"Hospital? What hospital?"

"The hospital in Nebraska City. After I was born, I came back to the farm and met Millie and Mabel, my twin sisters," Earl said with a big smile.

Morgan laughed and slapped his leg. "That's a good one, Earl. You really had me going. I swear. If you're not wiggling your ears, you're telling me some story to cheer me up. Now tell me—do you really have twin sisters?"

"Yes, I do. And I hope one of them sends me a cake while I'm here. Just to make sure, I plan to write a letter in the next day or two and remind them to send cake," said Earl. He crossed his arms. "And if you're good and don't beat me too bad when we play dominoes, I might even let you have some of my cake."

"Cake? Well, what are you waiting for? Get that letter posted and in the mail to your family—pronto," Morgan said excitedly. "Tell them I like chocolate the best."

Private Earl Young. Earl's suitcase collection.

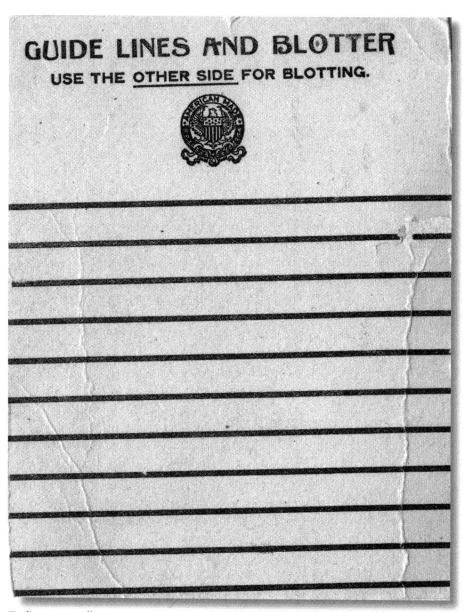

Earl's suitcase collection.

OFF TO CAMP.

MARCH, TWO-STEP.

MARCH, TWO-STEP 40	MANDOLIN & GUITAR 50	TWO MANDOLINS & PIANO .. 60
SONG 40	TWO MANDOLINS & GUITAR .. 60	ORCHESTRA .....
MANDOLIN SOLO 40	MANDOLIN & PIANO 50	BAND .....
TWO MANDOLINS 50		BANJO & PIANO .....

COMPOSED BY

J. A. SILBERBERG.

4.

Published by
NEW YORK:
40-61 WEST 28TH STREET. M. WITMARK & SONS. CHICAGO:
SCHILLER THEATRE B'LD'G.
LONDON, ENG.: TORONTO, CAN.:
CHAS. SHEARD & CO. WHALEY, ROYCE & CO.
Copyright 1901, by M. Witmark & Sons. Entered at Stationers' Hall, London, Eng.

2

Camp Humphreys

Reveille came early as usual the following day. The soldiers were several days into their routine. There was a lot of complaining. Soldiers complained about the meals. It didn't taste like the food they were used to at home. Some said the food didn't have enough salt. Others thought there was too much salt. Pushing and shoving broke out to settle a salt argument. One soldier lost his two front teeth over the matter. There was complaining about the physical work. There were too many heavy things to carry. They had to walk too far. They had to march too fast. They had to get up too early. They had to build bridges and had to do it too fast. Why did they have to do it day after day? They didn't like to dig the trenches so deep. They got too cold in the rain. They got too hot in the sun. They had to stand at attention for roll call in the morning. In the rain. They had to be at attention when it was 100 degrees at the end of the day.

Earl had a hard time understanding why there was so much complaining. He had volunteered, as many of the men around him had. The object of being there was to get training so they could do a job and do their bit to keep the Kaiser and the Huns from taking over the world. That's the way Earl saw it anyway. Sure, the food wasn't like his mother's food. But there was plenty of it. And they almost always got two slices of bread at each meal. So, things weren't so bad.

Earl had thought about his father and brothers and how he was raised. They were expected to work on the farm and not waste energy by trying to figure out how to get out of a job instead of just doing it. He was expected to pull his weight and help out. No doubt, it was hard work. He tried to meet each day by giving it his best. No matter whether that was milking cows, picking corn, chopping wood, hoeing the garden, or threshing wheat. You just did the best you could. That became his approach in the army.

Earl enjoyed learning about building bridges, and the army was giving him a free tour of the U.S.A. He had already seen or visited many states and cities that he had only seen on a map. He liked looking at his map and trying to figure out where they were and where they were going. In a way, the army provided a welcome change for Earl, more or less.

Each day was like the day before in many ways, but in many ways each day was a new experience—a new day to learn something he didn't know before. A new day to help get rid of that Kaiser. So, Earl didn't complain. He focused on the things that were new and interesting.

Envelope (front):
YMCA
"WITH THE COLORS"

Miss Millie Young,
Brock,
Neb.

Envelope (back):
Karl Young
Camp Humphrey
Virginia

Letter:

Cam Humphrey,
Virginia.
Aug 12. 1918 —

Dear Folks;

Well, this is the dawn of a perfect day for me, but lots of fellows here would wring my neck if I said so aloud so don't tell them.

Say, believe me, you never were in a real hot place, and never will be out there in good old Nebraska. It rains here every evening just [...] us at retreat, that is the last thing we do before supper. We all line up for roll call and there it begins to pour just long enough to cool is off. The red clay is sticky here if you get out of a path, other wise it is just as hard as a pavement

Earl Young
Camp Humphrey
Virginia
August 12, 1918

Dear Folks,

Well, this is the dawn of a perfect day for me, but lots of fellows here would wring my neck if I said so aloud so don't tell them.

Say, believe me, you never were in a real hot place, and never will be out there in good old Nebraska. It rains here every evening just in time to catch us at retreat. That is the last thing we do before supper. We all line up for roll call and then it begins to pour just long enough to cool us off. The red clay is sticky here if you get out of a path, otherwise it is just as hard as pavement, and as slick as a banana peel.

I arrived here Saturday evening in time for the first hot meal, since last Tuesday noon at Fort Logan. We ate all the cold corned beef, pork & beans, punch, "the best ever" coffee and jam.

That was a very nice trip for me, everything along the road being new to my sight. You might imagine what I saw along the road, but it would take a year to say it all. I might give you an imagination of the course of the trip: Denver, Brush, McCook, Humboldt, St. Louis, Louisville, Ky and I can't remember just the names of the other places. Charleston is one yet.

I am 17 miles from Washington D.C. On the Potomack river. I don't think this god's-for-saken place is on the map yet, just started last winter. This is an Engineers training camp but is entirely different from what you would imagine it to be.

They train an engineer, first with the pick and shovel, then the construction of roads, railroads, cement and other wise, regardless of the hot sun that registers 100 & 110 in the shade six hours a day. We get mostly shade work, for that is all there is here in this hot old hole.

This morning was my first duty here. They lined us up, about 500, in front of our barracks and marched for a mile to the southwest to the Potomack. When we reached the river, which is a couple of miles wide for the downstream a little piece and started across a bridge which reached only half way across, supported entirely by boats and not a post. We didn't know what was going to take place or where or when, only we felt kinda funny? Every step we took we bobbed up & down with the boats as we marked time.

When we reached the end of this half-constructed bridge, halt & attention was ordered of course, just in time? If I would finish this letter next time possibly you would feel just as I felt that very moment.

Well we're kindly told how to construct that bridge all the different parts all of the different knots to tie & to bind the thing together. Then we took it apart and put it back together in just a very few minutes. It proved to be very simple as well as easy but hot work out there. Also we took another apart and floated it down the stream a ways where we ate a cold dinner of macarona flavored good with tomatoes, rice & raisin pudding, punch, good water & butter beans. All you want. See—

After dinner some got the picks and shovels and some the job of putting the bridge back in place, some the hammer & saw on the new buildings, small but efficient. I with about 25 others went back to the heart of the camp to load up some logs to be used for a big permanent bridge for the river.

These bridges I spoke of are used in retreat or also in advance when we get in France. They can be constructed quickly and then

torn down and taken along so the Kaiser can't follow up as easy.
No lumber lost that way either.

This afternoon I was supposed to load up logs, but the wagons
didn't come until quitting time so we only loaded one load of eight
or ten logs all afternoon. Sunday I took a motor boat ride down &
across the river to Maryland, to a park - a beautiful one believe me.
Lots of loose girls down there. Loose in the upper belfry. I enjoyed the
ride though. Passed a big steamer on the way back. Was to Sunday
school in the morning. A chorus girl has been singing all evening
here in the Y.M.C.A. A little play on the stage but must go to bed.

Earl Young
Co. B
5th engr. Tran. Regt.
Camp Humphrey'
Virginia

Answer soon,
Earl

Earl Young, U.S. Army, A.E.F. Earl's suitcase collection.

Earl tucked away his letter and climbed up to the top bunk, passing Morgan who was already asleep, and for a change not snoring bad enough to keep Earl lying awake for hours. He was happy about that—and as he lay on his back, his mind recalled the show he had seen that evening. It was sponsored by the Red Cross at the Y.M.C.A. as most of them were. A group of chorus girls sang a medley of songs for the troops but one in particular stood out.

A song, that is, called *Song of the Soldiers*. It seemed to touch him in a deep place and, for Earl, the words were full of meaning and beauty. A girl named Emma sang it. She was pretty and blonde and reminded Earl of a girl in Brock, which only added to the beauty of the song.

"Song of the Soldiers"
A poem by Charles G. Halpine, 1864

Comrades known in marches many,
Comrades, tried in dangers many,
Comrades bound by memories many,
Brothers ever let us be!
Wounds or sickness may divide us,
Marching orders may divide us,
But, whatever fate betide us,
Brothers of the heart are we.

Comrades known by faith the clearest,
Tried when death was near and nearest,
Bound we are by ties the dearest,
Brothers evermore to be:
And, if spared and growing older,
Shoulder still in line with shoulder,
And with hearts no thrill the colder,
Brothers ever we shall be.

By communion of the banner—
Battle-scarred but victor banner,
By the baptism of the banner,
Brothers of one church are we!
Creed nor faction can divide us,
Race nor language can divide us,
Still, whatever fate betide us,
Children of the flag are we!

When the song ended, Emma introduced herself and said she was from Minnesota originally and became a volunteer for the Red Cross. One of her jobs was helping with a project to equip the SS *Red Cross*, nicknamed "The Mercy Ship," with emergency supplies.

Emma smiled and cooed at the soldiers. The boys were enthralled. She blew kisses and urged them to write their mothers and sisters to help the Red Cross. Specifically, she wanted the boys to ask their families to knit wool socks and sweaters for the troops and give them to the Red Cross, who would make sure they got to the soldiers when they went overseas. The Red Cross slogan was: "We cannot all serve in the trenches, but we can all serve at home."

The chorus girls passed out candy from The Sweets Company of America. Tootsie Roll candy was introduced to the troops. It was an instant hit with Earl. Cigarettes from the R. J. Reynolds Company were also handed out, and they were introducing a new packaged cigarette with the name of Camel.

Dreams and sleep were in short supply for Earl. Reveille was a rude intrusion into his dreams. The army had lots of work for Earl and the boys in his unit. The days started early, rain or shine. He thought today was another bridge building day. The army had planned each day to the fullest in order to train these boys from Nebraska and Michigan and Indiana and states all across America.

Earl had often told his friend Morgan, "You know that there's the right way and then there's the army way." The army wanted to take these plowboys and teach them how to build a bridge their way, the only way. If they could, it would be a vital function in the Allies' defeat of Germany.

Earl reminisced about last night, listening to the chorus girls sing. The Red Cross had made the evening very enjoyable. Now his clothes were soaked through and through with sweat, rain, and mud. The order had been announced that there would be no bridge building today. Instead, it would be the fine art of digging a trench. The army way, of course.

The boys worked diligently to construct the trench. Red clay stuck to their picks and shovels, as well as everything else. After a number of hours digging and re-digging, the officer in charge ordered the men into formation so they could practice marching. Marching in step with the other soldiers was hard enough but was even more difficult when you had to keep in step and in formation in Virginia mud.

"They Were All Out of Step but Jim"
A song by Irving Berlin, 1917

Jimmy's mother went to see her son,
Marching along on parade;
In his uniform and with his gun,
What a lovely picture he made.
She came home that ev'ning,
Filled up with delight.
And to all the neighbors,
She would yell with all her might:

"Did you see my little Jimmy marching,
With the soldiers up the avenue?
There was Jimmy just as stiff as starch,
Like his Daddy on the seventeenth of March.
Did you notice all the lovely ladies,
Casting their eyes on him?
Away he went, to live in a tent;
Over in France with his regiment.
Were you there, and tell me, did you notice?
They were all out of step but Jim."

That night little Jimmy's father stood,
Buying the drinks for the crowd;
You could tell that he was feeling good,
He was talking terribly loud.
Twenty times he treated, My! But he was dry;
When his glass was empty,
He would treat again and cry.

It made me glad, to gaze at the lad;
Lord help the Kaiser if he's like his Dad.
Were you there, and tell me, did you notice?
They were all out of step but Jim.

When the sergeant was satisfied that the marching had been somewhat successful, he ordered a break and announced "smoke 'em if you've got 'em."

"Say Earl, did you try one of those new cigarettes that the chorus girls passed out last night?" Morgan asked.

"The ones named Camels? Those were strange. Each cigarette was already rolled when you took it out of the package. I don't think they'll be very popular. It's just as easy to roll your own. It's amazing to me the things that people come up with," Earl said.

"I'll tell you something else amazing. The Camel cigarette was first named for Germany's Kaiser Wilhelm. The cigarette package showed the Kaiser in full imperial regalia, riding a white horse," Morgan stated.

"What? Named after that damn Kaiser! I won't smoke that brand," Earl exclaimed.

"Don't worry Earl," Morgan said. "The company changed their mind when they decided they didn't want to name their cigarette after a living person."

"I hope that Kaiser isn't living too much longer. Maybe they figured a lot of soldiers wouldn't buy cigarettes with a picture of the Kaiser on them," Earl said. "What could the company have been thinking?"

"That could be. However, the president of the cigarette company was quoted as saying he changed his mind because, and I quote: You never knew what the damn fool might do."

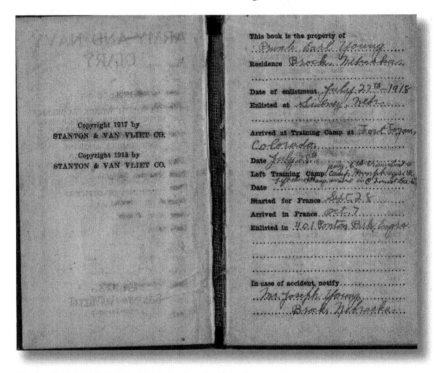

Earl enlisted on July 27, 1918, and arrived in France on October 7, 1918. Earl's suitcase collection.

3

Bobwhite

It had been raining since reveille and seemed to be increasing steadily. There could just as well have been the worst hurricane in Virginia history taking place. It didn't matter. The pontoon bridge instruction was scheduled for the day. This was the army and there was never a question about putting it off until tomorrow.

The troops located trees and used large, two man saws to fell the trees and broad axes to trim off the branches. That done, the next move was to take the trees down to the river. Or so Earl thought.

"Okay Morgan, which end of this hackberry do you want to carry?" Earl had asked, ready to go. "Let's get going so we can get out of these wet clothes," he said as he signaled with his arm.

"Wait a minute, Earl. You want just you and me to move this log? This hackberry must weigh three hundred pounds!" Morgan protested.

"Well it isn't going to get any lighter, and the longer it sits here in this rain, it will just get heavier. What a god-forsaken place today," Earl said as he shook the rain off his back.

Morgan began talking like he was explaining something to his little sister who liked to correct him with about everything he did.

"Moving the tree is not the problem, Earl. We just don't have any orders from the sergeant to move it yet," Morgan protested.

"Yeah, I guess you're right," Earl said as he looked at Morgan, the rain dripping off his helmet at a steady pace.

"You bet your summer's wages I'm right, plowboy. You've been in the army for almost two months now and should know we don't do anything without orders."

Earl had a rueful smile. "The army tells you when to get up in the morning. Tells you when to eat. When to shave. Tells you how to drive a boat. Tells you when to go to bed. And tells you which trees they want chopped down."

"The army even tells you when you can pick your nose, Earl. So don't go moving any logs around without orders."

After a pause, Morgan added: "Anyway, I heard they were bringing some horses up to help carry them down to the Potomac."

Earl and Morgan killed time using an axe to knock off the odd branch here and there from their hackberry. They were trying to look busy lest the sergeant get another idea that they could fell another tree. They had beaten the other men getting their trees down by a good 10 minutes. The order was given for a water break. The boys could sit in the mud. Or they could sit on the log in the rain. They each read the other's mind, shrugged their shoulders at the same time, and sat down on the hackberry.

"You've got some pretty good skills no matter what the army asks you to do," Morgan commented. How did you learn to do all those things?" Morgan asked as he handed Earl a water jug.

"I hate to brag, but I went all the way through eighth grade," Earl replied with a great deal of pride in his voice. "I was even lucky enough to go to college in January of this year at the University of Nebraska and pick up some good information that would help me be a better farmer," Earl said.

"No kidding? What did you study?" Morgan asked.

With that question, Earl felt a strange sensation. Morgan's question reminded him of the letter he had written just months ago to his brother, George, and George's wife, Laura, when he had been at school.

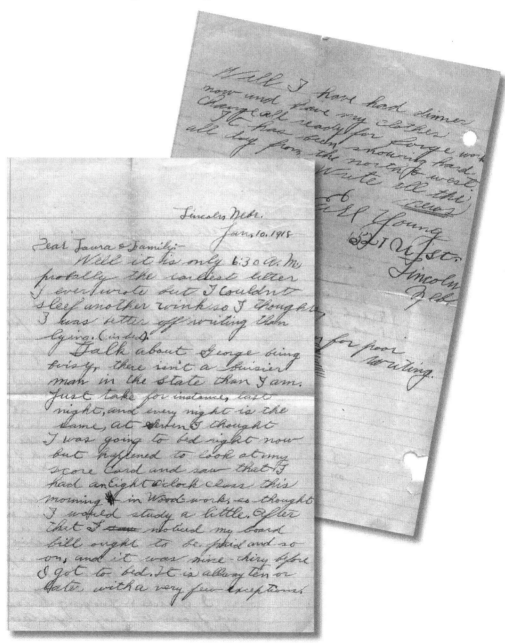

Lincoln, Nebraska
January 10, 1918

Dear Laura & Family:

Well it is only 6:30 a.m. It's probably the earliest letter I ever wrote but I couldn't sleep another wink so I thought I was better off writing than lying (in bed).

Talk about George being busy, there isn't a busier man in the State than I am. Just take for instance, last night, and every night is the same, at seven I thought I was going to bed right now but happened to look at my score card and saw that I had an eight o'clock class this morning in wood-work, so thought I would study a little. After that I noticed my board bill ought to be paid and so on, and it was nine thirty before I got to bed. It is always ten or later with a very few exceptions.

Well maybe I will be able to give you a pointer or two, as you say, but one thing sure: all of the Stuff (as Ed says), don't come by its self.

Take for instance Farm Management. I will just give you a problem. A farmer has 5 work horses. The cost for maintenance annually is: feed, $293.50; labor in caring for them, $70.30; shoeing & general expense, $4.90 and harness depreciation, $8.20. The horses were inventoried at $878.00 and depreciated in value, $35. Interest is charged on the investment at 6%. The horses work 963 hours each during the year. What is the cost per hour for horse labor???

In Dairy we have learned to test milk and cream and now we are learning to judge a milk cow, later we will look up pedigrees, judge cream separators and some more, don't know just what. Never milk any cows—

In Breeds & Judging classes we learn to judge beef steers & the like. In Woodwork we learn to use the square & Brain. In Forge the hammer and anvil & forge. I could say lots more if you were here. In wood work my grades average 80. Forge about 82 and don't know my others yet. I will send a scorecard along so you can just look at that and see what I am doing each day.

I was down to Charley's last Sunday. Emmetts hands are about healed now. Must close & eat breakfast. I suppose you are in the new house by this time. If so how do you like it.

Must Close
Earl
1521 U St
Lincoln

P.S. I dropped my pen, on the point, on the cement walk and almost ruined it.

Well, I have had dinner now and have my clothes changed all ready for forge work. It has been snowing hard all day from the north & west.

Write all the news,
Excuse mistakes, Blame the PEN for poor writing.

"Did you learn any useful things at the University? You apparently didn't learn how to stay out of the army," Morgan said and laughed.

"I learned about farm management, raising cattle, and . . . forge work," Earl replied. "For example, with the amount of rain that's falling on us, it would probably be enough to fill up a good size corn crib. I could calculate that." Earl had a look of satisfaction on his face.

"The amount of water in a corn crib—oh, that's real useful," Morgan said as he shook the water off his coat.

"Okay. I'll give you another example. I can figure how much wheat is stored in a granary or a bin," Earl said confidently.

"How do you calculate that?" Morgan asked.

"You figure what the volume of the building is. It's easy to figure for a rectangular barn. The volume is the length times the width times the height," Earl said. "It gives you the amount in cubic feet."

"I guess that makes sense," Morgan said as he pictured it in his head.

"Figuring the amount of wheat in a round bin is more difficult, but I learned how to do that too," Earl said.

"I guess you have time to tell me since we haven't been ordered off our water break yet," Morgan said.

"The volume is the height times the radius times the radius times Pi," Earl replied.

"Oh yeah? If you were wiggling your ears I'd know you're kidding me. And what does pie or cake got to do with your calculation?" Morgan joked.

"Not pie as in dessert. Pi as in the mathematical constant that is the ratio of a circle's circumference to its diameter, which is 3.14," Earl said. "See?"

"It's about as clear as trying to see my boots. They're covered in mud, so it's about as clear as mud," Morgan said, bewildered as to what Earl was trying to explain to him.

Morgan took another long drink of water. "I think I'll stick to history. I know some facts about that subject. You can have the math," Morgan lamented. "And another thing—if that sergeant doesn't give us the order to move off this log soon, I'm going to tell him where he can stick your Pi."

As Earl laughed, the sergeant gave the order to march to the river. The men learned more about bridge building that afternoon. The rain only stopped as they arrived back at their barracks.

"C and C?" Morgan asked Earl.

"C and C? What?" Earl said.

"Chow and then checkers?" Morgan said hopefully. "That is— as long as you don't talk about Pi anymore," he added.

The following morning Earl and Morgan were both on their second helping of biscuits and gravy. They were sitting next to a window watching it start to rain heavily. Again.

"Why does it have to start raining just before we have to go out and drill?" Morgan asked.

The sound of a bird caused Earl to look for it in the trees. "See that bird there Morgan?" Earl said. "That's a bobwhite. It's my favorite bird. This must be a sign that something good is going to happen today. There were quite a few bobwhite birds on the farm in Brock. I always stopped to find them in the trees when they called," Earl said.

"Bob White! Bob White!" Earl imitated the birds' distinctive sound.

Morgan looked around the room to see if any of the other soldiers were listening as Earl made his birdcall. Several soldiers were staring in their direction. Morgan thought about sliding under the table.

"I'll tell you what. If I get lost in the woods, make that weird bird noise so I can find my way out," Morgan said as he held his hands over his eyes. He hoped no one else could see him sitting at a table with this crazy guy making birdcalls.

"Bob White! Bob White!" Earl called even louder.

"If you don't stop with the birdcalls, they'll have me take you to the loony farm. On second thought, keep it up. If I take you to the loony farm we might get out of marching in the rain today," Morgan said.

The rain continued and splashed in the puddles.

"You know, I feel drenched just watching it rain. My boots feel heavy just looking at that mud," said Morgan.

"Speaking of mud—you want some more coffee?" Earl asked. "Might as well drink mud so we can get used to walking in it." Earl and Morgan sipped their coffee as they went from the chow hall to the barracks. Earl eyed Morgan's sweater enviously as Morgan put it on. He would have to write home and ask them to send him one.

"I bet my brothers, George and Julius and Ed, wish it could rain like this on their farms," Earl said as he tightened the cap on his canteen.

"Where do they farm? In Nebraska? What are the names of the towns they're near?" asked Morgan.

"George has a wheat farm in western Nebraska, near a town called Dalton. He just bought some land thirteen miles west of there, near two other towns: Potter and Dix. Julius and Ed work in eastern Nebraska yet, near my hometown of Brock. They'd like to buy some land near Brock but it's too expensive. Land there costs over four hundred dollars an acre! But you can buy raw, native farm ground in western Nebraska that has never been broke out. George is trying to get Julius or Ed to farm out there," Earl said. "I've always been interested in farming. After the war, I might go to western Nebraska and raise wheat," Earl added.

"What is the ground like there?" asked Morgan.

"There's a lot of land in Nebraska that's still just native grass—and some places where entire counties have never been farmed. It all needs to be broke out yet," Earl said. "And not many trees. Just put a plow behind a tractor or a team of horses and go until you think it's time to turn around and go back."

Plowing wheat stubble. Earl's suitcase collection.

Harvesting wheat. Earl's suitcase collection.

"What are those cowboys and ranchers going to say when you plow up all their land?" Morgan said, walking into the barracks.

"It's funny you mention that. The times they are a'changing. I remember reading a poem in the *Sidney Telegraph* about what the cowboys thought of the farmers breaking up their virgin soil," Earl continued. "As a matter of fact, I liked that poem so much that I cut it out of the paper and I brought with me," Earl said.

Earl walked over and pulled out a book from under his bunk. "I've just been using it as a bookmark."

"Let me see that book," Morgan commented as he looked at the cover. "Hmmm, *The Rural Text-Book Series of the Breeds of Livestock*."

Morgan had a perplexed look on his face and said, "You are a plowboy through and through, aren't you?"

"I find it interesting. This is one of the books I had at the University of Nebraska," Earl said. "Don't start making fun of me or I won't show you this poem."

"Oh, alright. Let me read the poem," Morgan said. "I can always find something else you say to make fun of."

"The Cowboy's Farewell to the Dryland Farmer"
A poem by H. Fred. Birks, 1918

A cowboy lay out on the prairie,
He said it was all off with him.
He had two quarts of good whiskey
And nearly a full quart of gin.

His saddle he used as a pillow.
His blanket he used for a bed
And when he awoke from his slumber,
These words to himself he then said:

Farewell, you scissor-bill farmers!
You're driving me far from my home.
You've homesteaded all of the country,
Where the slick-cars and mavericks roamed.

No more we'll be able to rustle,
As in the old days gone by—
Then he took a big drink from his bottle
Of good old '99 rye.

I've been all my life in the saddle;
All I know is how to rope an old cow,
And I never could work on a sheep ranch—
And I'm damned if I'll follow a plow.

There's no other job I can handle,
There's no other life I'd enjoy
Away from the spurs and the saddle—
A wild and wooly cowboy.

Farewell, dear old Montana country,
The fairest green spot on God's green earth.
I'm leaving this grand state forever,
Going far from the land of my birth.

Here's luck to you all, you dry-landers,
Who've "settled" this country at last,
And I hope you'll succeed in the future,
As the cowboys have done in the past.

Morgan finished reading the poem and handed it back to Earl.

"You're right. That's a good poem. It about sums up how things change, doesn't it?" Morgan said.

"The ranchers pushed the Indians off their land. The Indians pushed other Indian tribes off their land before that. Then farmers pushed ranchers off their land. So, who's going to push the farmers off their land?" Earl asked.

"Good question. I don't know," Morgan said as he scratched his head.

"I don't know either. Just as long as it isn't the Kaiser!" Earl said.

The boys looked out the window of the barracks. The rain was running steadily off the roof. They took their time getting their gear. No sense in standing out in the rain and mud until absolutely necessary.

"How much rain do they get in Nebraska?" Morgan asked.

"In Cheyenne County, about fourteen inches a year."

"Fourteen inches? In Michigan we get that much in a month," Morgan said. "Cheyenne County—must've been named after the Cheyenne Indians that lived there at one time."

"That's right, Morgan. It's the real West out there. In some ways it's still the Wild West," Earl replied.

"When I think about the Wild West, I think about Wyoming," Morgan said. "Actually, it sounds to me like Cheyenne County, Nebraska, should have just been part of Wyoming from the get-go."

"You know, a lot of Nebraskans would totally agree with that Morgan," Earl said as he buttoned his coat and headed outside into the rain.

Today the army decided it would teach the men how to dig a proper trench. Earl, Morgan, and the other soldiers dug in the mud. They made sure the trenches were the correct specifications. Not too deep. Just deep enough. Not too wide. Just wide enough. Not too long.

Rain continued to fall and the two wet soldiers passed the time telling one another about their families and their home states. A remarkable bond was forming. Thank the army or thank their two families who raised men like the two of them. Men who were not afraid of fighting for their country. Men whom the army was testing to see what they were made of to make sure when they went to France, they would do whatever the order was. No wavering. No questions. No second guessing. Just following orders. And looking out for each other. Soldiers like Earl and Morgan were forming a bond so tight, they could have been brothers.

Trench digging, or mud digging, went on. The boys were getting a lot of practice. They listened to the bobwhites and woodpeckers and dozens of other birds that lived near the Potomac. They saw and heard birds they had never seen or heard.

Of the two, Morgan was usually the one asking questions, whether they were training or playing checkers. As the trench digging went on, Morgan wanted to talk about school again and asked Earl more about it.

"Like I said, I got through pretty much all of eighth grade —when it ended rather abruptly," Earl said, rather embarrassed.

"Why? What happened?" Morgan asked as he tilted his head, unsure of what kind of a response to anticipate.

Earl got quiet, then explained: "I was overdue with getting an essay back to the teacher on time. The teacher said 'bring that essay back tomorrow or don't come back.' So, I did—never went back that is."

"You just never went back to school? You're kidding, right Earl?" asked Morgan as he stopped digging to ponder this amazing halt to Earl's education.

"It's the honest truth Morgan. No kidding," Earl replied. He stood still for a moment.

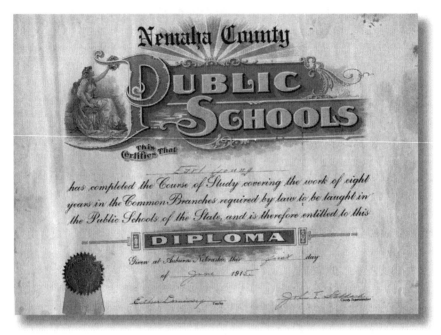

Earl's eighth grade diploma, June 1, 1915. Earl's suitcase collection.

Earl and Morgan stared at each other while the wind drove rain into their faces. They both shrugged simultaneously and resumed digging the trench. Sensing that Morgan had run out of questions for the time being, Earl spoke up.

"How much schooling have you had Morgan?"

"I completed seventh grade and just a few weeks after that my father got thrown by a horse and broke both his right arm and right leg. I started helping more with the things that he couldn't do while he recovered. There was so much work to do I never went back in the fall. My father said he was planning on having me quit school soon anyway, even before he got hurt," Morgan said. There was a sense of duty as he spoke.

"He said I could add and subtract. I could spell pretty good. So that was that and my school days were over."

"Well that explains it, Morgan!" Earl said loudly.

"Explains what?"

"Explains why you don't like to write letters. I went all the way through eighth grade and that's where they teach you how to write letters and how to mail them. You didn't go to eighth grade, Morgan, so you just didn't learn how," Earl said with a grin. He stood up to shake a gallon of water off his back.

"Didn't learn how to write, eh? You always say something to make me smile, rain or shine," Morgan said.

"And the other thing is you have to find enough work to earn two cents to mail a letter when you do write one," Earl said.

Morgan didn't ask questions after that.

"What are you going to do if we make it back from France?" Earl said.

"I've thought about having a farm. Maybe stay in the army. I dunno," Morgan said. He paused and then spoke again, "You know I just realized something. The army is teaching us how to build bridges, right? So, I guess since I have all this knowhow. I'll just cross that bridge when I come to it."

Morgan tried not to laugh at his own joke but couldn't hold it in. His giant laugh rolled through the woods. Earl laughed almost as loud as Morgan. "Look who's cheering who up now."

It wasn't just raining anymore. Thunder shook the ground. "I think the mud is getting heavier out here. Where are those horses? With all this rain making all this mud, tomorrow promises to be as rough as today. Another day of mud. Mud that clings to your boots. Mud that gets in your socks. Mud that makes your feet cold like wet cement. Mud that makes it that much harder to dig a trench or build a road," Morgan said. "Mud, mud, mud, mud!"

"You think you've got it bad? What about me? All this mud affects me a lot more than it does you, Morgan," Earl preached.

"And just how does it affect you more than me?"

"My shoe size is eleven E. You're only a nine B. An eleven E holds a lot more mud than your dainty foot," explained Earl.

"Well, you got me there," Morgan said, then snorted.

"Do all those older brothers of yours have big feet too?"

"Actually, my brother Julius does, believe it or not."

"Julius. Isn't that the brother that you said something the other day about going into farming with?" asked Morgan.

"Yeah. As you say, I'll cross that bridge when I come to it. After I take care of that Kaiser! I have a bayonet just for him!" Earl clenched his jaw tight for a few moments as he considered dispatching the Kaiser in different ways. He shuddered, lost in thought momentarily. Was it the Kaiser who made him shudder? Or just the rain? He shook those thoughts away and answered Morgan's question.

"Julius has an opportunity to buy some farm ground that's never been broke out. Can you imagine that? Miles and miles of buffalo grass that could be plowed under and planted to wheat. Then there'd be miles and miles of wheat to thresh."

"How do they clear all those trees?"

"Trees?" Earl said as he looked around at the forest of trees in front of them. "There are no trees on the prairies of Nebraska. In Brock we're always clearing trees, probably just like you had to do in Michigan all the time. But in Cheyenne County, Nebraska, you'd be hard pressed to take one of those Red Cross gals on a picnic and find some shade."

The two soldiers were starting to get cold, shaking more gallons of water from their coats. Army coats were heavy to start with and gained a lot more weight when they soaked up rain. Just as Morgan started to say something else, their sergeant made the decision to move out. It was getting dark and the horses were apparently lost or just not coming. There was now some discussion they were also lost, and some argument about which direction to go to get back to Camp Humphreys. Most of the men didn't have a clue. They all started to go into the woods in different directions, including Morgan.

But Earl knew the right direction. He called out, "Bob White! Bob White!" and started off back to camp.

"I recognize the sound of that bird," Morgan yelled as he located Earl and hurried to catch up to him, as did the rest of the men.

"How do you know for sure, Earl?" one of the men had asked. "In this weather if we guess wrong, some of us won't have to worry about fighting Germany. We won't make it out of Virginia alive."

"I don't have to guess," said Earl determinedly. "I just know the way. Follow me."

And he was right. They even made it back to camp and in time to have supper. Such was army life and each and every man knew *tomorrow would be much like today had been.* A lot of the men were feeling very down just thinking about it. But not Earl. He had just received a letter from Julius.

Dear Brother,

Will write you a line to let you know I am still on deck, following the plow and harrow.

You no doubt know that men 18 to 45 will register soon, so perhaps I can go across with you. I thought you enlisted in the Infantry de Corps. Why the change?

We are not sending the card spoke of in this letter, because it pertains only to those in the Army who can ride – that is 21 yrs. of age.

The fellow you bought the old motorcycle from wants to buy it now. What is your price? Better sell it before the rats carry it off: for I shot all the dogs some time ago.

Wish you would send us your insurance policy, so we could see what it says and then put it in the bank for you. What is your pay there? Do your best and stick to it. It is hard work on the farm as we can't get help. The corn doesn't amount to much.

Julius

Langford motorcycle in repair shop, July 3, 1915. Earl's suitcase collection.

Julius had mentioned in his letter that the man Earl bought his motorcycle from would like to buy it back. He wasn't sure he would sell it. It was an Indian motorcycle, American made. The color was a deep red. And it could reach 40 mph if he pushed it. Earl remembered reading about "Cannonball" Baker, who rode an Indian motorcycle from San Diego to New York in 11 days, 12 hours, and 10 minutes.

The Indian was the first motorcycle produced in the U.S.A. The first year it was manufactured was 1901. Now that America was in the war, the Indian company sold most of its motorcycles to the army, and civilians found they were in short supply. Earl liked the Indian motorcycle magazine ads. Their motto was "North. South. East. West. You're on the right road."

Earl reasoned that the motorcycle might come in handy to run over the open prairie when he returned to Nebraska. After he whupped the Kaiser. As chance would have it, the army did just the opposite as the soldiers had expected—there wouldn't be any marching in the mud today. The boys gathered in a classroom and were instructed for the first time on the correct way to construct a pontoon bridge. The army way.

Earl went to sleep that night satisfied with his decision to volunteer instead of waiting for the draft. In his letter, Julius had said that men up to 45 years of age would have to register. Earl felt the timing for him had been good, even considering the circumstances that led to his impulse to join up. Morgan had asked him how old he was and Earl had told him he was underage to be sent overseas. Morgan had wanted to hear how he was able to join the army since he was underage but Earl had avoided that conversation. Since he had come to know Morgan though, Earl made the decision to talk about it soon.

"My name is Major DuPries. I learned about engineering at West Point. Listen up, plowboys. Today we talk about pontoon bridges. A pontoon bridge is a collection of boats or floats, connected together to cross a river. This works on the Archimedes principle. Each pontoon can support a load equal to the mass of the water it displaces. And the load also includes the mass of the bridge itself. If the maximum load of a bridge section is exceeded, one or more of the pontoons become submerged and will proceed to sink. This is unacceptable."

To emphasize his point, he slapped a riding crop onto the table. Earl flinched at the noise, as did most of the other soldiers in the room.

Major DuPries continued, "The Archimedes principle states that the upward buoyant force that is exerted on a body immersed in a fluid, whether fully or partially submerged, is equal to the weight of the fluid that the body displaces, and it acts in the upward direction at the center of mass of the displaced fluid. What happens if the weight of the water displaced is less than the weight of an object on the pontoon? It sinks. Which greatly displeases the soldiers now on the bottom of the river."

The Major was quiet while he allowed the boys some time to grasp what he was telling them. He took a gulp of coffee then continued, "Now picture yourself in France. Your orders are to build a pontoon bridge over a river for the infantry to move heavy artillery."

He paused long enough to look directly in the eyes of the soldiers to judge their commitment. "If you don't build the bridge correctly, precious time and resources are lost. It may even be decisive in the outcome of a battle. Or lives lost. So, we are going to teach you how to do it. And then we teach you how to do it faster," Major DuPries concluded. He put his hands on his waist in superman fashion, clapped a loud clap, then grabbed his coffee to drink the last sip. "Now grab your gear and let's go build a bridge."

The doughboy engineers had paid attention to Major DuPries in the classroom. They were fast learners and each soldier had the attitude that if pontoon building was what the army and Uncle Sam were asking them to do, then they were going to do it right and to their best to support the war effort. Earl enjoyed this new adventure in engineering. He looked forward to explaining to his brothers in his next letter about the Archimedes Principle and telling them that his Expeditionary training regiment broke the record for building a pontoon bridge in the fastest time.

The regiment did so well that by four o'clock that afternoon they had been released for the remainder of the day. The army knew which soldiers were going to be the men they wanted to build the bridges. Those who didn't have the skills for this kind of work were transferred to other duty assignments. Earl, Morgan, and 171 other privates were given the AS patch to sew onto their uniform. The "Advanced Sector" shoulder patch indicated they were part of the American Expeditionary Force that specialized in supporting front line combat units.

Morgan and Earl proudly sewed the AS patch on the right shoulder of their uniform and, of course, played checkers on their time off. Checkers allowed them to relax, talk, and be ready to see the vaudeville show later that evening. Earl sat more erect with a purposeful look, as he frequently glanced at the bright red Cross of Lorraine symbol in the center of the patch.

Earl Young's U.S. Army Advanced Service shoulder patch. Earl's suitcase collection.

"Before we start our game, there's something I want you to read," Morgan said. "I saw this in the *Suffolk News-Herald*. Since you shared a poem with me, I thought I'd share this one with you."

"Old Montana"
A poem by Cory J. Campbell, 1910

Take me back to old Montana.
Where there's plenty room and air;
Where there's cottonwood an' pine trees,
Bitter root an' prickly pear;
Where there ain't no pomp nor glitter,
Where a shillin's called a bit,
Where at night the magpies twitter,
Where the Injun fights were fit.

Take me back where the sage is plenty,
Where there's rattlesnakes and ticks;
Where a stack of whites cost twenty,
Where they don't sell gilded bricks;

Where the old Missouri river,
An' the muddy Yellowstone
Make green patches in the Bad Lands
Where old Sittin' Bull was known.

Take me where there ain't no subways,
Nor no forty-story shacks;
Where they shy at automobiles,
Dudes, plug hats an' three-rail tracks;
Where the old sun-tanned prospector
Dreams of wealth an' pans his dirt,
Where the sleepy night-herd puncher
Sings to steers an' plies his quirt.

Take me where there's diamond hitches,
Ropes an' brands an' ca'tridge belts,
Where the boys wear chaps for britches,
Flannel shirts an' Stetson felts.
Land of copper an' alfalfa!
Land of sapphires! Land of gold!
Take me back to dear Montana'
Let me die there when I'm old.

"Well, it looks like I might have started something when I let you read that poem of mine. Something that I'm already regretting," Earl teased as he began placing the checkers on the board.

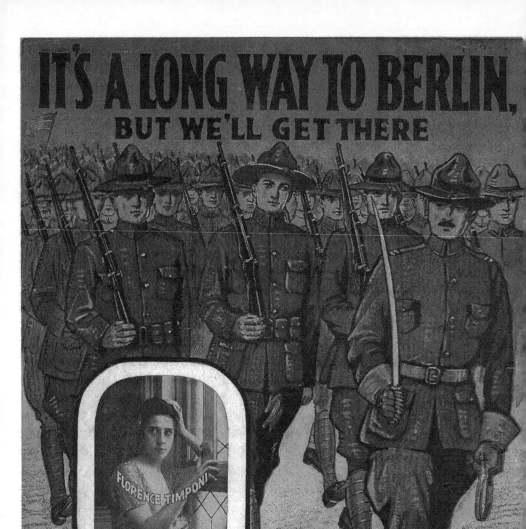

4

It Was Wheat or War

"It's a Long Way to Berlin, but We'll Get There"
Song lyrics by Arthur Fields, music by Leon Flatow; 1917

Rueben Plank a husky Yank,
Came into town one day,
And said, "I can't resist,
I really must enlist—by heck,
I'll help to get that Kaiser Bill
I hear so much about."
He passed the test, threw out his chest,
And started in to shout.

"It's a long way to Berlin, but we'll get there.
Uncle Sam will show the way,
Over the line, then across the Rhine,
Shouting Hip! Hip! Hooray!
We'll sing Yankee Doodle 'Under the Linden'
With some real live Yankee pep! Hep!
It's a long way to Berlin, but we'll get there,
And I'm on my way, by heck—by heck."

Rueben Plank was in the ranks
For just a little while,
Then he soon went ahead,
He's Corp'ral Plank instead, by heck.
He gets his squad together,
And at night when all is still,
They sing the chorus Reuben wrote,
To Mister Kaiser Bill.
It's a long way to Berlin, but we'll get there,
And I'm on my way, by heck—by heck."

Written on back of checkers box: Pvt. Earl Young, 401st Pontoon Park Engrs., A.E.F.
Earl's suitcase collection.

The army issued every soldier a cardboard checkerboard with red and black cardboard circles when they arrived at Camp A. A. Humphreys. The board was labeled "Trench Checkers."

Morgan always picked the black pieces and Earl always let him have his winning color. There was that bond—a quiet comradery. Even in trench checkers.

"It's great to have some extra time off, eh Earl?" Morgan said as he made his first move.

"Very unexpected. And very welcome," Earl agreed.

"I'm surprised you agreed to play checkers instead of writing a letter."

"I figure it won't take that long for me to beat you in a few games. I'll have time to write afterwards. I'm anxious to find out if the wheat came up okay. I also want to ask them how the threshing bee got along. It's probably happened by now."

Morgan stopped placing the checkers on the board. He tilted his head and asked, "What do you mean they planted their wheat already? And what the heck is a threshing bee?"

"Let me explain a few things about farming in western Nebraska. It's completely different than the way crops are grown in eastern Nebraska. Or Michigan," Earl said.

"I'm all ears," Morgan replied.

"Then can you do this—" Earl said. He wiggled his ears and laughed.

"No, I can't wiggle my ears. I think you are the only soldier in the entire army that can do that, Earl. Quite th useful talent. Maybe you can get a job in a vaudeville show after we're discharged."

"Okay. Here's how wheat is grown—in Cheyenne County anyway. You're probably used to wheat being planted in the spring. Out west, there are wheat varieties that farmers seed in the fall, usually in September. If they're lucky, they get a little rain shower that helps it come up and start growing."

"There's more than one kind of wheat?" Morgan asked, perplexed.

"Yeah—I helped my brother George plant a variety called Turkey Red," Earl said.

"Turkey Red? Are you pullin' my leg?" Morgan asked.

"No. It's for real. Turkey Red is what is called a hard red winter wheat. It was first brought here from Russia. You plant it in

September. It lays dormant through the winter then it starts growing in the spring and gets harvested in mid-July," Earl explained.

"Russia's already been in this war for a couple of years. We're allies with them, ya know. So when we get to France, you can shake a Russian's hand and thank them for your wheat," Morgan said.

"I'll thank them for the wheat," Earl said, "but I'll have to inform them about a problem that came with it."

"What's that?"

"The Turkey Red was a great crop for the plains. But the seed they brought with them also had Russian thistles," Earl said.

"And Russian thistles are weeds," Morgan added, nodding his head.

"They are huge weeds and become tumbleweeds, which can be real problems to try to deal with," Earl said.

Morgan finished setting up the game and made his first move. Earl took his turn, still thinking about the wheat. "See, you harvest the Turkey Red with a binder in July. Brother George has a new, modern McCormick binder. It cuts the wheat stalks then binds 'em into sheaves with twine. The sheaves are stacked and stored in a barn until the fall, when they can be threshed."

Earl started to move a checker, then changed his mind and moved another one. He continued, "Then in the fall, a day is set aside for a farmer to have a threshing bee. One of the farmers brings his threshing machine. Lots of people are needed to get everything done in one day. Farmers and their wives come from miles around to help."

Earl went to move a piece but pulled back again. "The farmers load sheaves of wheat in a wagon then use a pitchfork to throw the sheaves into the thresher. The thresher knocks the wheat kernels off. The wheat is piled up on one side of the thresher and the wheat stalks on the other side. Some of the farmers store the wheat in a granary. Others bale the straw. Meanwhile, the women are all working hard to prepare a huge meal. The wives have already brought with them pies and cakes. Then they start cooking all the meat and vegetables. When the threshing is done, they all gather together at a huge table for a feast."

"I'd sure like to go to a threshing bee someday," Morgan said.

"I can still picture the one I was at last year," Earl said. "The noise of the thresher was incredible. Belts screaming. Billows of smoke and steam. Flying wheat stalks. The screech and growl of machinery. Horses rearing up. The wind blowing the straw in your eyes and ears. Wheat chaff sticking to the sweat on the back of your neck. The itch of the chaff down your shirt. The smell of barbeque beef and coffee mixing with the aroma of the wheat and the smell of apple wood from a kitchen stove. The men, all trying to work harder than the others. The laughter of the women. I miss it already."

Threshing bee time. Earl's suitcase collection.

Earl made a double jump with a red checker, swiping up two of Morgan's black checkers in his hand. "That's what a threshing bee is like." He paused just a second and said, "King me."

Morgan rubbed his chin and studied the board. "What do you hear from home?" he asked as he made another move.

"Got a letter from my brother, Julius, yesterday."

Earl thought about Julius as he tried to determine whether to make another jump to take one of Morgan's pieces. His mind went over a conversation he had with Julius when he had left Brock and traveled to western Nebraska to help his brothers with the wheat harvest—just before he decided to enlist.

Harvest had just about ended after almost 10 days of starting and stopping the wheat cutting. Rain showers forced them to stop the McCormick and wet grain became a real problem. When it was dry enough for them to start cutting again, they would work long hours until past dark or until a thunderstorm forced another stop. And there was always the chance the thunderstorm would bring hail. Hailstorms were capable of mowing the wheat down just as if a giant scythe had come out of the sky.

Wheat fields in Cheyenne County were huge. Some fields were 160 acres of wheat. Earl discovered that if he stood in a low spot in a field he could look in all directions and see nothing but wheat. He had been told that wind made the wheat wave just like waves in the ocean. He hoped to be able to see that for himself when he crossed the pond.

Earl decided his game move and jumped a black checker, taking it off the board. He had been reliving the conversation with Julius in the harvest field and wasn't paying much attention to the game. He winced as he saw Morgan complete a triple jump.

Earl thought about the day he helped his brothers with harvest just a couple months ago. There were only about 30 more acres of cutting to take care of and wheat harvest would be complete for the year. And then one of those thunderstorms sprang up just as Earl was driving a truck into the field. Julius was on the new Sandusky tractor, pulling the McCormick binder. He had about a half load of wheat sheaves. The rain made a hissing sound as it hit the muffler on the Sandusky.

The Gold on Nebraska's plains. Earl's suitcase collection.

Julius had hopped into the passenger side of the truck to get out of the rain.

"Guess we'll have to stop for a while and see how much rain we get. If it rains too much, we can wait an hour or two and try to finish up," Julius said, as he took off his large cowboy hat and started to roll a cigarette.

"I've been wanting to talk to you anyway," Earl said. His tone was serious.

"Okay, little brother. Guess we'll have some time to do that right now."

Julius waited for Earl to say something. Earl had frozen up and all he could do was swallow hard and stare out the windshield. The words wouldn't come out.

Julius gave Earl a pat on the arm as he said, "You're thinking about going off to fight the Kaiser, aren't you?"

"How'd you know?" Earl asked, surprised that Julius could read him so well.

"I have to say you've been mighty contemplative the last few days. I figured it was one of two things. A girl or the Kaiser," Julius said.

"It isn't any girl, Julius. Wish it was."

"I figured you were contemplating joining up. Both George and I have thought we'd wait until we got drafted. George especially. He told me that he and Laura are expecting their first baby. I'll get drafted sooner than he will more than likely."

"I'm happy about George and Laura. I'd like to be here when they have the baby. I think I'd like being an uncle," Earl replied.

Julius Young and friend. Earl's suitcase collection.

The two brothers sat there in the truck quietly. They watched the wind rustle the golden wheat. Julius took a drag from his cigarette and blew smoke through his nose. Earl gripped the steering wheel of the truck with both hands. He took one hand off the wheel, made a fist, and slammed it as hard as he could into the seat of the truck. "That damn Kaiser has to go! I can't make any future plans as long as Germany is trying to take over the world. I can't think about being an uncle. I can't plan to grow my own wheat. Or even think about marrying some girl!"

"I might wait to make some decisions," Julius said. "Looks like I'll be in that second tier of conscription. I'll wait and see what happens. My plan is to go back to Brock when George is finished with his farm work."

"Well. I've decided that this may be a good time for me to leave. Harvest is almost over and I won't have a job too much longer," Earl said.

"It's a tough decision, Earl," Julius said with sympathy in his voice. "I'm sure this last week has got you all stirred up."

"There's a lot of talk around the dinner table at night with the harvesters. The war has everyone frightened and unsure just what they should do about it. A lot of men are trying to decide if they should enlist or wait until Uncle Sam makes the decision for them," Julius said, as he finished off the last of his cigarette.

"I've made up my mind. I'm going to join the army but I don't exactly know how to go about it," Earl said with a perplexed look.

"Heck, it's still sprinkling. Just enough to make the wheat too wet to cut anymore today. So, what else to do but have another cigarette. When the rain stops, I better have a look at the left front wheel on the tractor. Sounds like a bearing might be going out. If so, someone could drive into Sidney for the part before the store closes," said Julius.

"I just thought of a question, Earl," said Julius: "How are you going to join the army? You're too young to enlist without getting the folks' consent. And you'll need it in writing."

"I've thought about that. I think I can just go into Sidney since that's where the county seat is. I'll sign some papers. They'll probably just take my word for it. I'll just tell them Pa said it was okay."

That night at dinner most of the hungry harvesters started on the second helping of mashed potatoes. Laura made them with coffee-ground gravy, one of her specialties. The conversation was the war this. And the war that. Again. There was a lot of debating and the talk was getting more impassioned.

Laura spoke up in frustration, "All you men ever talk about are two things—and they both start with W!"

"What two things Laura?" said George.

"Wheat. And War!" She stood up abruptly and marched into the kitchen.

Earl realized he really wasn't paying attention to the checker game. He saw three black kings on the board. It was pretty much a rout in Morgan's favor.

"Well Morgan, you beat me again. Those black checkers you always play with must be luckier than the red ones I use," Earl said as he lamented.

"Beating you at checkers is easier than shooting ducks in a barrel, Earl. You start thinking about Nebraska and then your mind wanders—next thing you know I'm crowning another king," Morgan observed. "What were you just thinking about?"

"Wheat. And war. Wheat and war," Earl stated as he reminisced how frustrated Laura was with the harvesters at the dinner table that night.

"Wheat and war? Well, the war won out over the wheat for now, Earl," Morgan said as he jumped another red checker and took it off the board.

"Yeah, for now." Earl just sat back in his chair with his arms crossed.

"Tell me how a plowboy like you ended up in Virginia in the army," Morgan asked. "You could be in Nebraska at a threshing bee."

"Since we're such good checker playin' buddies, I'll tell you how I ended up at Camp Humphreys—courtesy of the army. There was an incident back in Nebraska. It's what got me here—to the Army Expeditionary Force. I haven't told anyone. Not my folks or my brothers. Not anyone about what happened," Earl said as he shook his head. "The whole thing is hard to explain."

He looked into Morgan's eyes to determine how much trust was there.

"When I decided to enlist I was hoping to be trained as a motorcycle dispatcher," Earl said. He watched Morgan's blue eyes.

"One day a plowboy. The next, a motorcycle dispatcher," Morgan kidded.

Earl folded up the trench checker set and put it in the box. Next time he'd have to pay more attention to the game and stop talking so much about Turkey Red and threshing bees.

"Here's how the story goes, Morgan: The army wouldn't let me enlist to go overseas because I was too young. I was in Sidney, Nebraska, the Cheyenne County seat, and didn't have any proof of who I was or how old I was. I needed the help of my folks to prove my age."

Sidney
July 21, 1918

Dear Folks,
     *Well, I suppose you have received my telegram by this time but
no answer yet. 7:30 p.m.*
     *Please have this filled out and sent back by return mail regard-
less of weather. If it reaches here by the 25th so much the better. If
not I go to Fort Logan, Colorado for my suit, vaccination and so
forth and then to a motorcycle training school somewhere in the
U.S.A. It makes no diff. to me just so I can do my bit.*
     *Going to Dalton by train this morning and ride my horse
home 8 miles & spend the remainder of the day in selling him. He
is sure a good one. 8 miles in 45 minutes isn't a bad record for 100
in the shade.*
     *I can't feel alone in the work before me so don't worry. I will
see some of the world, get a furlough once in a while and eat.*
     *George has his wheat all cut by this time & sure is good, be-
lieve me. I was just examined 10 min. ago and pronounced sound
as a dollar.*
     I must get breakfast a bit for the train.
     Send this answer to:U.S.A. Army
                         R.S.
                         Sidney, Nebr.

With Love,
Earl Young
Dalton, Nebr.

     *There won't be much use to write to me at Dalton for I prob-
ably wouldn't get it.*

"There was one delay after another that went on for a week. I was getting anxious and just wanted to start in the army as soon as I could. I had owned a motorcycle of my own when I lived in Brock. It was an Indian Powerplus—eighteen horsepower. I could handle it really good. I just knew I could ride an army motorcycle too, and ride dispatches back and forth to the front. But first I had to actually get in the army. It was a long, long week of waiting and checking at the recruiting station every few hours to see if the folks had sent the army the information they needed," said Earl. "I just wanted to get an army uniform to help get rid of that damn Kaiser! I wanted it more than anything I've wanted in my whole life. But if I just sat around waiting on the army to get all their papers in order, the war would be over before I got to do my bit. I didn't want to just dream about being a soldier, I wanted to be a soldier."

Villeneuve's collection in <u>One Hundred War Cartoons</u>; George Colburn, cartoonist. Cartoons were also printed in the "Idaho Daily Statesman," starting in 1914, and continuing during WWI.

5

Soldier's Dream

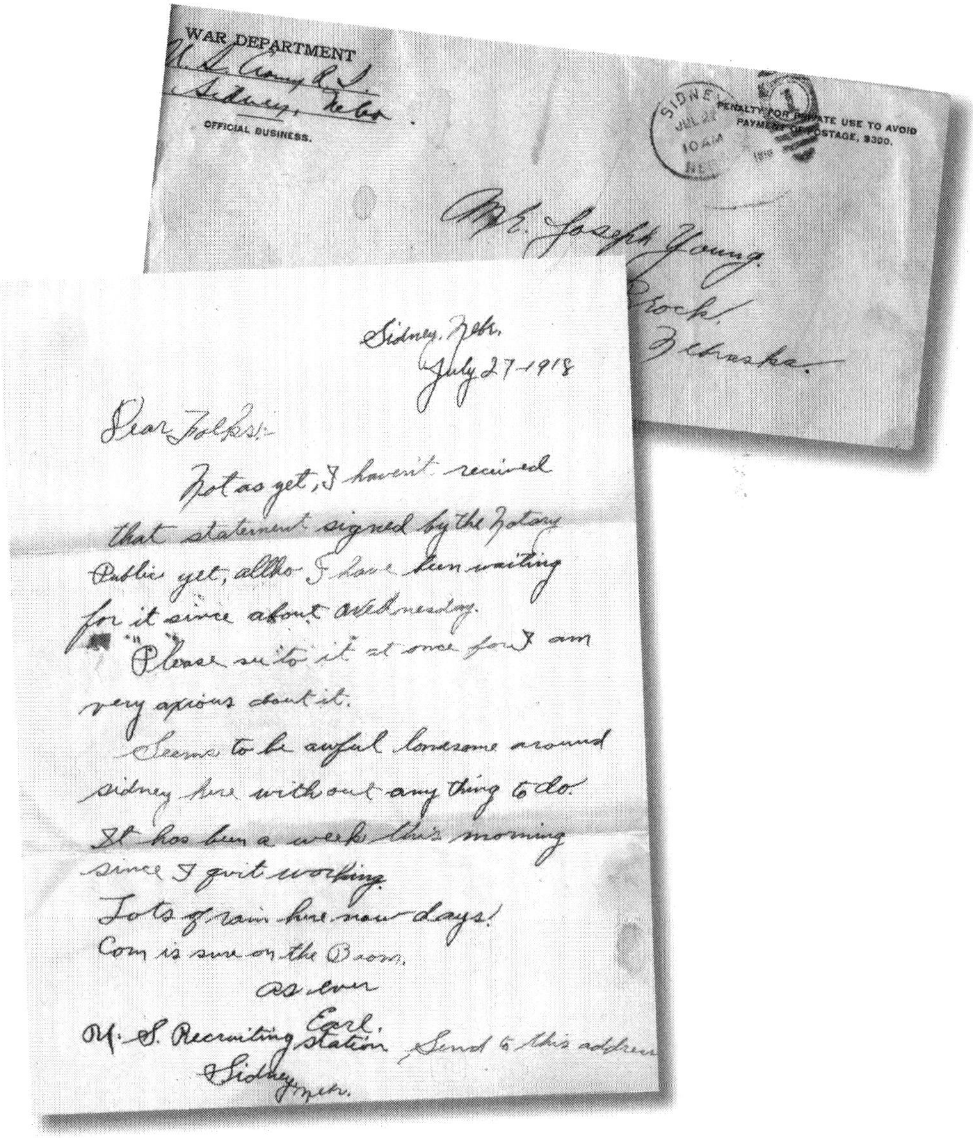
WAR DEPARTMENT
U.S. Army R.S.
Sidney, Nebr.
OFFICIAL BUSINESS.

SIDNEY JUL 27 10 AM 1918 NEBR.

PENALTY FOR PRIVATE USE TO AVOID PAYMENT OF POSTAGE, $300.

Mr. E. Joseph Young
...rock,
Nebraska.

Sidney, Nebr.
July 27-1918

Dear Folks:-

Not as yet, I haven't received that statement signed by the Notary Public yet, altho I have been waiting for it since about Wednesday.

"Please see to it at once for I am very anxious about it.

Seems to be awful lonesome around Sidney here without any thing to do.

It has been a week this morning since I quit working.

Lots of rain here now days!

Corn is sure on the Boom.

As ever
Earl.

U.S. Recruiting station
Sidney, Nebr.
Send to this address

Sidney, Nebr.
July 27, 1918

Dear Folks,

Not as yet, I haven't received that statement signed by the Notary Public yet, although I have been waiting for it since about Wednesday.

Please see to it at once for I am very anxious about it.

Seems to be awful lonesome around Sidney here without anything to do.

It has been a week this morning since I quit working.

Lots of rain here now days.

Corn is sure on the bloom.

As ever,
Earl

Send to this address
U.S. Recruiting Station
Sidney, Nebr.

"I kept thinking maybe they couldn't find a notary anywhere. Maybe they think getting their crops in is more important than writing to the recruiting station in Sidney. I thought maybe Mother had been talking my father into dragging his feet so I wouldn't get to fight at all before the war was over and done. I finally decided to get Corporal Weeks at the recruiting office to send them a letter," Earl said.

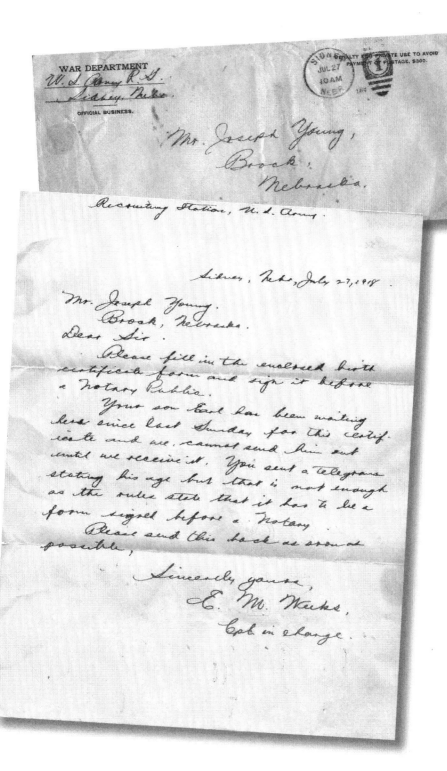

WAR DEPARTMENT
W. S. Army R.S.
Sidney, Nebr.
OFFICIAL BUSINESS.

Mr. Joseph Young,
    Brock,
        Nebraska.

Recruiting Station, U.S. Army.

Sidney, Nebr., July 27, 1918.

Mr. Joseph Young.
    Brock, Nebraska.
Dear Sir.
        Please fill in the enclosed birth
certificate form and sign it before
a Notary Public.
        Your son Earl has been waiting
here since last Sunday for this certificate and we cannot send him out
until we receive it. You sent a telegram
stating his age but that is not enough
as the rules state that it has to be a
form signed before a Notary.
        Please send this back as soon as
possible,
                Sincerely, yours,
                    E. M. Weeks,
                        Cpt. in charge.

Recruiting Station, U.S. Army
Sidney, Nebr.

WAR DEPARTMENT
U.S. Army R.S.
Sidney, Nebr.
Official Business
July 27, 1918

Dear Sir,
    Please fill in the enclosed birth certificate form and sign it before a Notary Public.
    Your son Earl has been waiting here since last Sunday for this certificate and we cannot send him out until we receive it. You sent a telegram stating his age but that is not enough as the rules state that it has to be a form signed before a Notary.
    Please send this back as soon as possible.

Sincerely yours,
E. M. Weeks,
Cpl. In charge

*Scout Troop, Brock, Nebraska, September 27, 1913—Earl Young, 2nd from right;
E. E. Briggs, Scoutmaster*

*Villeneuve's collection in <u>One Hundred War Cartoons</u>; George Colburn, cartoonist.
Cartoons were also printed in the "Idaho Daily Statesman," starting in 1914, and
continuing during WWI.*

"My mother really didn't want me to enlist but Father kept telling her I was old enough to make my own decisions. They got the
certificate notarized and arranged for a special trip to Nebraska City
to get everything correct. Finally. Finally, the certificate arrived so I
could enlist. I'm sure those recruiters never saw anyone so persistent
as me to get into the army."

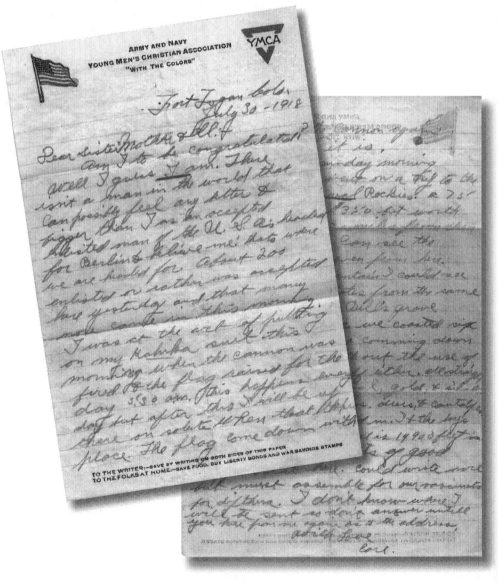

Fort Logan, Colo.
July 30, 1918

Dear Sister, Mother & All:

Am I to be congratulated? Well I guess I am. There isn't a man in the world that can possibly feel any better & bigger than I as an accepted enlisted man of the U.S.A.; headed for Berlin & believe me! That's where we are headed for.

About 200 enlisted or rather was accepted here yesterday and that many more came in this morning. I was at the act of putting on my Kahika suit this morning when the cannon was fired & the flag raised for the day 5:30 a.m. This happens every day but after this I will be up there on salute when that takes place. The flag came down with the report of the cannon again at 5:45 I think it is.

I arrived here Sunday morning and four of us went on a trip to the mountains. The real Rockies. A 75 mile trip. It cost $3.50 but worth $50.00. We are 15 or 20 miles from there here in camp but can see the big snow peaks even from here.

From Look out Mountain I could see foure different states from the same rocks with Buffalo Bill's grave about 10 feet from one. We coasted six miles at one time coming down this mountain without the use of the engine & no bluff either. All straight goods. Saw old coal, gold & silver mines. Buffalo, elks, deers, & antelopes altho they were fenced in.

I & the boys walked up one peak that is 14,900 feet in altitude. I get lots of good stuff to eat here. Could write more but must assemble for our vaccination for dipthera.

I don't know where I will be sent so don't answer until you hear from me again as to the address.

With Love,
Earl

6

A Piece of the Rhine

"We Don't Want the Bacon (What We Want Is a Piece of the Rhine)"
Song lyrics and music by "Kid" Howard Carr, Harry Russell, and
Jimmie Havens; 1918

If you have read your hist'ry,
Then you're bound to know
That we have always held
Our own with any foe.
We've always brought the bacon home,
No matter what they've done,
But we don't want the bacon now,
We're out to get the Hun:

We don't want the bacon,
We don't want the bacon.
What we want is a piece of the Rhine.
We'll crown Bill the Kaiser
With a bottle of Budweiser.
We'll have a wonderful time.
Old Wilhelm the Gross will shout, "Vas is Los?"
When we hit that Hindenberg line. Fine!
We don't want the bacon,
We don't want the bacon.
What we want is a piece of the Rhine.

When first this war began,
They said we had no chance.
They couldn't figure how
We'd get our men to France.
But they will soon discover,
Uncle Sam is out to win.
We've got the Fritzies on the run,
We're headed for Berlin.

The possibility of another checker game was pretty much forgotten as Morgan was very intrigued by Earl's story. Morgan began gathering up the checkers and said, "Can I ask you about the incident—you know, what happened that pushed you to enlist?"

Earl clenched his jaw tight. "It all happened on that same day I was talking to my brother, Julius, in the harvest field. Remember our conversation in the truck while we waited out the rain? We'd continued to talk and it continued to rain. We couldn't cut any more wheat that day so George sent me into Sidney to get a part for the Sandusky tractor. I drove into town, got the part, and stopped off at the Sidney Mercantile. I also needed to get some new gloves because I had worn holes in the other ones. Handling all those wheat sheaves is hard on the hands.

Almost as soon as I stepped into the Mercantile, these two ranchers started giving me a hard time. They said they knew my parents were German immigrants. They were saying stuff like, 'Why don't you just go back to Germany if you like Germans so much? Why don't you just stick some sauerkraut under your armpits so you can smell more like a kraut?' I tried to ignore them but they kept after me. The storekeeper even started in! He was saying he wasn't going to sell any gloves to somebody that supported Germany in the war.

"Now there were three of them confronting me! They accused me of not being a true American. There was no sense in arguing with them. It was getting more confrontational. When I said I wasn't leaving without the gloves, the storekeeper picked up a rake. He said if I didn't leave his store right away he'd use the rake. Use it on my thick German head."

Morgan stopped gathering up the checker pieces. Earl had his full, undivided attention.

Earl continued: "The ranchers said I probably just wanted the gloves so I could build stuff for the Kaiser. Then I'd ship it to him! Help the Kaiser? I hated the Kaiser. The Kaiser was responsible for causing this problem for me, causing problems for other guys with a German background. I tried to reason with the ranchers and the storekeeper that the Kaiser was causing problems for all Americans, regardless if their background was German and that the same German families who enjoyed their heritage and culture also hated the Kaiser.

"For them to say I was helping the Kaiser was too much. I got angry and shoved the rake out of the Mercantile owner's hand. I yelled at the ranchers, 'What can I do to prove to you that I hate the Kaiser and everything he stands for? What can I do to prove to you that even though my ancestors came from Germany, I support America in the war?' The largest of the two ranchers backed up a few steps and pointed out the store window to the building across the street. I could read the sign. It said U.S. Army Recruiting Station. He said, 'Enlist. Right now.' Without really thinking about it I said I will, if you will."

"I waited that long week to get my folks' permission and the notarized certificate. And that's how I ended up a few days later in Fort Logan, Colorado. A private in the U.S. Army."

Morgan looked stunned and could hardly think of anything to say. It was an amazing story. To agree to enlist by uttering five simple words—*I will if you will.*

Morgan waited a few moments trying to think about what to say. Then he spoke his thought: "You said you hoped I'd understand." Morgan stuck out his hand to shake Earl's hand. "I understand completely," he added.

Then with a big smile on his face, he made an announcement: "Well Earl, you certainly could be the poster boy for that song you hear nowadays."

He cleared his voice and his baritone voice sang:

> *"You're in the army now.*
> *You're not behind the plow.*
> *You'll never get rich,*
> *By diggin' a ditch,*
> *You're in the army now."*

Earl took a deep breath and let it out slowly. He said, "And as you might expect Morgan, when the army sent me to Ft. Logan, Colorado, the first thing I wanted to do was write a letter home to my family."

"Of course you did," Morgan said, as he placed his hands on either side of his head, overwhelmed thinking about how often Earl wrote letters. *How can one man write so much!*

ARMY AND NAVY
YOUNG MEN'S CHRISTIAN ASSOCIATION
"WITH THE COLORS"

Fort Logan, Colo
July 20: 1918

Dear sis & all;

I am a soldier now &
not behind the plow, is the
popular song here amongst the
boys.

I suppose that you would
like to know what overtook me
to bring me here any way Thats
what the western people said
when they heard that I was
going to leave so suddenly.

Well, I am here and glad of
it too. I got here 10:00 am. sunday,
had our bunks assigned and were
told that we could go for a
little ride through the Rockies
and back through Denver. It only
cost $3.50 for the seventy five
mile trip & now take it
from me it sure is nice to have

Fort Logan, Colo.
July 30, 1918

Dear sis & all,

I am a solgier now & not behind the plow, is the popular song here amongst the boys.

I suppose that you would like to know what overtook me to bring me here anyway. That's what the western people said when they heard that I was going to leave so suddenly.

Well, I am here and glad of it too. I got here 10:00 a.m. sunday, had our bunks assigned and were told that we could go for a little ride through the Rockies and back through Denver. It only cost $3.50 for the seventy five mile trip & now take it from me it sure is nice to have the privilege chance to see the mountains. Real Mountains. Just think?

We can see the old snowy peaks about 20 miles to the west of here. In fact in plain sight of where I am sitting at a west window of the little frame Y.M.C.A.

A French lesson has just been completed and now the player piano is going.

About 50 boys writing letters somewheres just as I am. Paper & envelopes furnished as you will see by the stamped paper.

We get lots to eat here. Was vaccinated for typhoid & small pox this morning. Typhoid is "taking" or rather making my arm so sore that I can hardly write & can't raise it to my shoulder.

I was to go on a 2 hour hike this after noon but nix on this arm stuff. Several fellows fainted but nix on that stuff for me.

I probably will be transferred from here Friday or Sat. I en-listed in the Mechanical Corps or rather in the Quarter Master Corps. I don't know where I will get my training possibly in Texas,

California, or New York. Nobody knows until we start. In fact, I don't care. I am well satisfied. I took my civilian clothes off yesterday and won't put them on until I see Berlin. The Damn Kaiser, dead!!

Will send my suitcase in a day or two. Wish I had a regular kit. No handy place to get them here & besides they cost seven times as much here as there. Will you get one and send it? To my next address?

I could sit & write all day but must go to mess. Tell them all hello for me.

Earl

I am 8 miles south west of Denver.
I slept all afternoon to have a rest.
Mighty cold nights. Sleep in tents on cots & two woolen blankets.
Will get my finished pictures tonight.

Good By
Will give you an address in a few days which I can't do now.
Earl Young

"That's a remarkable story, Earl. Just remarkable. It sounds like you had it in the back of your mind to enlist all along but those fellows in Sidney aggravated you enough to force it," Morgan said. "My story isn't as wild as yours, Earl. My father kinda wanted me to enlist. Things were skimpy on the farm and he was hoping I might leave to find some other work. So the army provided that. I signed up one day and the next I was off to do some training. You know, I just thought about this. I probably really should let my folks know where I am. What do you think, Earl?"

"Do I understand that you didn't even tell your mother you enlisted?" asked Earl incredulously. Morgan tilted his head to look at the ceiling and shuffled his feet. "Write them! As soon as you can, Morgan," Earl said, shaking his head in disbelief.

Morgan changed the subject: "Your folks knew what you were up to with trying to enlist. What about your brothers in western Nebraska? How'd they find out you enlisted in such an all fired hurry?" Morgan asked.

"Funny you should ask," Earl said as he made a writing motion with his arm.

George and Laura (Dirks) Young. Earl's suitcase collection.

Fort Logan, Colo.
August 1, 1918

Dear Brother & Family,

I can't think of anything just now to write but will try it a little anyhow.

I got to Denver last saturday night about 10 p.m. but stayed there all night & shipped out here the next morning. This is about 8 miles southwest of Denver. Denver is sure a pretty sight when the lights are on. We are a lot higher here.

The first unusual thing that I noticed after leaving Denver was the Mountains. They lie about 20 miles to the west of here. They look to be two or three miles from here. It seems so funny after getting here, had two blankets & a spring cot issued to us in one of the big bunks, we were told that cars were waiting down below to take as many, of our bunch about 50, that cared to go to the mountains on a 75 mile sight seeing trip. Only foure of us volunteered, just making a jitney load. We traveled & traveled some more and still they looked to be just a mile or so away. Finally after an hours ride over the finest kind of roads, as they all were all the way, we hit the reall truly mountains.

We went up a canyon beside a rushing stream for about 15 miles on low gear most of the time and making it hum some too. All kinds of fishermen and travelers camping along the stream. Lots of bungaloes, the prettiest ever hanging over the roads and amongst the pine trees that cover the mountains.

We reached the height of 14,900 feet. Also was on Lookout mountain where Buffalo Bill is buried. Without moving out of our states we could see grain fields in tracks distinct that looked to be the size of a big house, but with the "glass" we decided that there was 10 or 15 acres in them.

We coasted 6 miles down this mountain with the engine shut off.

Must go & stand for Retreat. 5:45 p.m. The flag comes down and the cannon goes off.

Bang it went.

I didn't get to finish this right before that and haven't had time or ambition since. On Tuesday morning they called us at 3:15 & by 3:30 there were about 39 of us marched down to the kitchen to help cook and stayed there until 8:30 p.m.

Now believe me I can appreciate a little sleep today. I am in the last barracks so better get to bed before we leave. They take 50 to 100 hrs. to go by train & where to. This is just a receiving fort here.

How is that threshing getting done? Is yours done yet? How is Paul? Is he sick yet. How do you like the picture I sent? I suppose you have seen Harrs by this time. You can send that trunk home I guess. If it isn't large enough to hold all just put the rest in a store box.

A free show today & tonight at the Y.M.C.A. Lots more to write but so tired I can't see straight. The flies are bad & hot to sleep. Must try anyhow. Answer soon. And get Laura to write too.

Brother,
Earl Young
19th Company
Ft. Logan, Colorado

"I'll tell you some more about the last few nights I had on the farm in Dalton," Earl said, looking at Morgan. "Wheat harvest was about half over and going pretty good. We'd had a pretty good day without too many breakdowns. It was late, about 10:30 at night, before all the men had gathered around the harvest table."

Earl leaned forward, rubbing his head, as if to make the words he was going to speak become clearer.

"Laura had been busy in the kitchen, getting supper ready for all the men," Earl continued. "Guess she was upset. She was as tired as the rest of the harvest crew after a long day in the hot sun. She brought out a big ham, coleslaw, corn on the cob, baked beans, and squash.

"'Wheat and War!' That's what Laura said. She put the mashed potatoes on the harvest table with a bang, looked straight at George and said, 'Wheat and War!'"

"I think I understand," Morgan commented. "She probably just wanted some other conversation. She was tired of the constant talk each night about how many bushels an acre the wheat was making and how many krauts the men would kill when they enlisted."

"Yeah," Earl nodded his head in agreement. "Poor Laura, out there on the farm with no other women. Sometimes my sister, Millie, was there visiting. But usually Laura was there all by herself with having to feed twelve to fifteen hungry men. Three or four times a day."

"Just growing boys, as my father would say," Morgan said.

Both men paused, thinking how both of their lives changed in just a few weeks. A month ago neither one of them had ever heard of Camp A. A. Humphreys. After a bit, Morgan asked, "What were some of the other conversations like around that harvest table?"

"Hmm, that night Laura was upset, some of the harvesters were talking about how some of the towns in Nebraska were changing their names—changing them so they didn't sound like German names," Earl said. "A harvester called Shorty told us about a town in Nebraska that was named Germantown. Recently the town had changed its name to Garland. One of their local boys, Roger Garland, had died in France. So they named the town after him."

"Seems like a number of towns in every state are changing their names so they don't sound German," Morgan said, shaking his head. "I can tell you about a town in Michigan. There was a community of German-Lutherans and the town was called Berlin. The name was changed to Marne."

"Marne? Sounds like a French name," Earl said.

"That's right, it is French. The Battle of Marne took place just outside of Paris in '14. It was a great victory for our side. The Frenchies and the Brits whupped the German Army in that fight. Because of that win, France today is still fighting for its freedom over the Kaiser."

"I read in the *Nemaha County Herald* that Nebraska also had a town that changed their name to Otoe."

"Otoe—like in automobile?" Morgan asked.

"No, not automobile. Otoe, as in Otoe Indian, a Native American tribe that lived in that part of Nebraska," Earl corrected.

"Guess the folks in Nebraska felt the same way as the folks in Michigan," Morgan said. "They didn't like their town name being the same as Germany's capital."

"When the Kaiser decided to make all this trouble, it sure made it hard for all the Americans living here with a German background, didn't it?" Earl said.

"I blame the Kaiser. What's his name? Kaiser Wilhelm, or whatever, for all the misfortune of the good people here that still have some association with Germany. Just because that's where their ancestors are from don't mean they support everything Germany is doing," Morgan said.

"But, just like those men in Sidney, the ones who confronted me, there are lots of people in the good ole U.S.A. that think if you have a German anything in your background then you are loyal to Germany, not America," Earl said.

"Yeah. You proved them wrong, Earl. I can tell you that there's a number of boys in our barracks that can tell a story about enlistment that is pretty similar to yours," Morgan said.

"I don't doubt that a bit. I'm sure we're all a lot alike—so proud to be part of this American Expeditionary Force that they could bust their buttons. I can tell you this. There is not a soldier in this camp any prouder than I am," Earl said.

And with that, the men finished their checker game. Morgan had played with the black checkers again. And won. They played a second game without saying a word. Earl won that time.

"That's enough checkers for today, Morgan," Earl said. "I've got to get a letter written and in the mail to answer a prayer."

A Mother's Prayer for Her Boy Out There

WORDS BY
ANDREW B. STERLING

MUSIC BY
ARTHUR LANGE

5

JOE MORRIS MUSIC CO.   145 W. 45th ST.,   NEW YORK

7

Mother's Prayer

"A Mother's Prayer for Her Boy Out There"
Song lyrics by Andrew B. Sterling, music by Arthur Lange; 1918

Beside a vacant chair she's kneeling,
When the lights are burning low,
Way down in her heart the feeling,
That only a mother can know.
And in the peaceful silence,
By the vacant chair,
She softly says her evening pray'r.

Just a little pray'r, when shades are stealing,
Just a little pray'r, a voice appealing,
To a baby's shoe clinging,
While the Angelus is ringing,
Come the words that start,
From an aching heart,
"May angels guard him tenderly, tonight,
And send my baby back to me."
That's a mother's pray'r,
For her boy "out there."

"My country needs me now," he told her,
"Mother darling I must go."
Tho' he's fighting like a soldier,
He's only "her baby" you know.
And while her tears are falling,
By the vacant chair,
She softly says her evening pray'r.

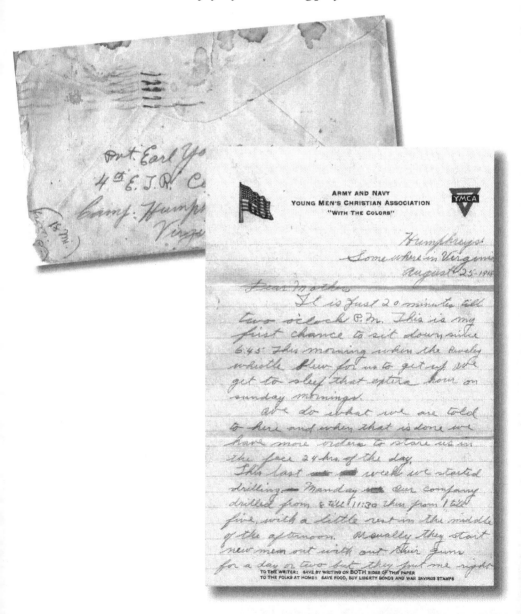

Private Earl Young
Co. C. 4ᵗʰ E.T.R.
Humphreys
Somewhere in Virginia
August 25, 1918

Dear Mother,

It is just 20 minutes till two o'clock p.m. This is my first chance to sit down since 6:45 this morning when the Revelry whistle blew for us to get up. We get to sleep that extra hour on sunday mornings.

We do what we are told to here and when that is done we have more orders to stare us in the face 24 hrs. of the day.

This last week we started drilling. Monday our company drilled from 8 till 11:30 then from 1 till five, with a little rest in the middle of the afternoon. Usually they start new men out without their guns for a day or two but they put me right through the mill with the gun on the shoulder.

The rifles we use weigh 11 lbs. Can you imagine the raw sores that old prince gets on his shoulders & neck?

Well I was nearly as bad the first night, then tuesday they put us to digging trenches for the water works like they dug in Johnson. The soil is a real sand mixed with rock the size of a hen egg. It takes a pick to get this stuff loose.

This camp is 12 miles square and there is about 30,000 soldiers here. All Engineers and all get the same training. The size will give you some idea of the work to be done here, being a new camp just started last January.

Everything is new. It seems to me they just started up the Potomac River & when they ran out of gasoline they stopped for *supper and while on the bank someone, some <u>nut</u>, said lets build a camp here & call it A.A. Humphreys. There isn't any name for the hills, ditches & trees of all kinds, a tree within reaching distance of one another.*

Wednesday I went back on the drill grounds again with my rifle & sore shoulder which I shan't forget in a day. Thursday I was put on "K.P." or rather Kitchen Police, that is a helper in the kitchen. Peeling spuds with a butcher knife & scrubbing floors, tables & the like. We all get our turn at this unwished for job from 4 a.m. till 7 or 8 p.m.

Friday we drilled & Saturday is a sort of holiday. In the morning we have inspection and little odd jobs to do just as they happen to be. To stand inspection, which every soldier, marine, sailors stand means that we all fall in a column at attention with rifles. That means, toes apart, heels together, belly in, chest out, head & eyes up and chin in. We do all of these stunts in a second or 1/100th of a second and not a move, not a sway of the body, not a spit & not a sneeze or fighting any flies or bees.

The lieutenants say it tests our will power to let a wasp sting you on the nose and never dare to raise the hand to fight him off. Pretty tough sometimes but nice to talk about after it is over. If we make a mistake or do a thing too slow or too quick while drilling we get what might be called a cussing with possibly some double time, or running back & forth across the drill field with the gun on the shoulder. If you don't run fast enough to suit the Lieutenant he may cuss & send you again & etc. Not much pleasure to army life in times of war, not here anyway.

On inspection day the shoes, leggings, trousers, shirt, hat & especially the rifle must be absolutely clean from all specks of dirt

& grease. I cleaned one rifle last Sunday and was transferred to another Co. & Regiment here this morning & now I have another to clean up.

They are more strict here than over in the other regiment wear I was.

I have been in camps for foure weeks today since I hit Fort Logan, Colorado. There wasn't a one that liked it at Logan but this is seven times worse than there. Oh well, I can stand as much as anybody & a good deal more than lots of the fellows.

Drilling isn't hard for me compared as to these Virginians that never saw the inside of a garbage can. The officers asked a man just in front of me yesterday where he was, & by jinks, he really knew that he was in the army. Lots of them just like him from the mountains, you know, and never got any further. They all look & talk just as alike. You ought to see the negroes here. They have part of the camp to themselves. All educated boys you know. They have the reputation of being the happier ones. A fellow can stand & laugh at their conversation until he chokes.

There is something going on at the various Y.M.C.A.'s every evening. We go to bed at 10 p.m. The time is an hour earlier here than it is there. And 2 hrs. earlier here than Cheyenne time.

Do you hear from the west very often? You might send George's and Mabel's letters to me if you will if there is any news. I sure like to get a letter better than anything else.

The fellow in the next bed here got a package containing a cake, some cigars & matches & several jars of jelly. Of course, as they all do, they all eat until it is all gone. I haven't had but one piece of cake in the last six weeks until now, except what the Harr girls gave me before I left.

If you can find time to bake a big cake for a big one makes a fellow the best friend until someone else gets a larger one then he is second.

If you bake the cake, I'll bet the treats that Dad can manage a box of cigars in one corner. What did the rest of the folks think that I enlisted?

I would rather be where I am than be worried by the draft that is sure to come. What does Julius think about this next draft. Tell him to join anything except the Engineers Corps if he is drafted.

I guess I will half to close & clean this new rifle I got this morning. How do you like that pennant I sent you. They have larger & nicer ones here but I can't afford it. The pay days aren't very regular here for some reason or another. I get $30 a month less $6.50 insurance. They are supposed to send that policy to you. See the local recruit station at Auburn if it hasn't reached you yet. Everyone has one just like it.

I guess I will practice digging real war trenches & putting on the gas mask this next week. We go through real chambers where the gas is and find out what we can expect when we see the gas coming over there. A bunch was called out yesterday, fellow that I came with from Logan, for oversea exams. Others have been here for three months & haven't been examined for "overseas" yet.

Answer soon,
Your Sammy boy
Earl
4th E.T.R. Co. C
Camp A.A. Humphreys, Virginia

P.S. Well this is Tuesday, noon. Just had dinner, plum full to the brim and then some.

Didn't get this mailed Sunday evening as I intended. Another soaking rain last night. I got some C.C. pills for my cold this morning. Everything is loose now.

Say, will you send me some gun rags. We half to keep those guns shining like a silver dollar. You can open that suitcase the best you know how. I lost the key. Hand my suit in a dark place where it will keep clean & pressed.

Send quite a few good strong rags of any kind. We half to buy towels & tear them up. Awfully expensive when they cost $.50 a piece.

Tell them all hello. When will Ed be called.
I have got the drill down pretty good now. Started bayonet drill yesterday. I will get a shot in the arm for typhoid fever tonight, so I will never get it or smallpox either.

Where is Millie? Is Miss Hardin still in Brock?

I like the army a little better each day but sometimes I feel pretty punk. Especially when there isn't any mail.

Send the Auburn paper when you get it read each week.

Must go to the drill grounds now with guns & bayonets.

Earl Young

Earl's letter writing stoked his appetite as much as being on guard duty for 24 hours. The soldiers that night were served roast beef, liberty cabbage, peas, onions, baked apples, and apricot pie.

"What's liberty cabbage, Earl?" Morgan asked when they were in line to get their chow.

Earl quietly whispered in his ear, "You know—it's the new name for sauerkraut since we can't say sauerkraut anymore. That German word upsets people to the point of bloodshed."

"That's taking things too far. When they change names around food, it just doesn't taste the same," Morgan lamented.

Earl and Morgan were pleasantly surprised when they found out they would not be getting their typhoid fever vaccinations that evening. So what do soldiers do with extra time on their hands? Get additional sleep? More rest so they could march faster tomorrow? The boys decided the best way to take advantage of this extra time would be entertainment at the Red Cross after dinner. There was a vaudeville act but Earl's favorite part of the evening would be listening to a Red Cross volunteer sing a song called "Just Before the Battle, Mother."

"Just Before the Battle, Mother"
Song lyrics and music by George F. Root, 1863

Just before the battle, Mother,
I am thinking most of you,
While upon the field we're watching,
With the enemy in view—
Comrades brave are round me lying,
Fill'd with tho'ts of home and God,
For well they know that on the morrow,
Some will sleep beneath the sod.

Farewell, Mother, you may never
You may never, Mother,
Press me to your heart again;
But oh! You'll not forget me, Mother,
You will not forget me, Mother,
If I'm number'd with the slain.

Oh, I long to see you, Mother,
And the loving ones at home;
But I'll never leave our banner,
Till in honor I can come.
Tell the traitors, all around you,
That their cruel words, we know,
In ev'ry battle kill our soldiers,
By the help they give the foe.

Not Sauer Anymore

April 22, 1918

Soon one of America's favorite sides may come to the front.
Sauerkraut could become 'Liberty Cabbage'. Produce dealers
across the U.S. feel the change is imminent and will help
Americans identify with the enormity of the task in front
of us. A favorite on the dinner table and on the street corner,
Sauerkraut is getting back to its roots and reminding
us all, it's all about liberty! Some worry it will take more
cabbage to buy America's favorite cabbage but that myth
can be laid to rest as Peter Stillforth of Western Produce
Markets tells us: it' is time to keep your heads, prices will not
be going through the roof! That's right folks, don't fret;
what was once sauer is now fresh and crisp and full of liberty

8

Liberty Cabbage

It was another hot day in Virginia. A rain shower during the night made the air feel like you could wring water out of it. That was only partly right. For the boys on their 12-mile hike, with extra weight on their packs, it was like wringing sweat out of the air. This was the army however, and those 12 miles weren't going to wait until tomorrow. And the drill ordered for today was 12 miles out. And 12 miles back to camp.

About mile 10, a soldier fainted. Then two more fainted from dehydration shortly after that. Three boys slowly went down on their knees. As one of them attempted to stand again, he tumbled over and rolled 10 yards into the woods. The ninth soldier who went down like a boxer had given him a one-two punch. The lieutenant wisely decided it was time for a break.

Earl was in pretty good shape due to the physical work he was used to doing. Farmers stayed fairly active from sun up to sun down. Although he was tired, he wasn't exhausted. Morgan was also capable of marching a long distance without falling down.

"It seems to come as a big surprise to some of the fellas that you've got to be in good shape to endure the rigors of army life," Earl said. He took a drink from his canteen.

"There's a saying . . . the army separates the men from the boys. I'd modify that to say the army separates the farm boys from the rest of the pack," Morgan said, then placed a pinch of chewing tobacco in his mouth.

"You know, it would be a challenge for Daniel Boone to march and find his way through these Virginia woods," Earl said.

"It was Daniel Boone that said all he needed in life was a good gun, a good horse, and a good wife," Morgan said then smiled broadly. "I agree it'd be a challenge even for that frontiersman. I need to correct part of your statement though. Daniel Boone was born in Pennsylvania and lived in Kentucky. He spent some of his life in North Carolina and West Virginia. But technically he wasn't ever in the state of Virginia."

Earl looked at Morgan with astonishment. *I'm just trying to make some conversation and here Morgan is, sitting like a professor on this log, lecturing me. Daniel Boone in West Virginia, not Virginia. Technically. Morgan is being a bit picky. Or maybe I should have learned my history better.* As Earl tried to recall some of that history, he had an idea.

"Technically I am right Morgan. When Daniel Boone was living, West Virginia wasn't a state yet. West Virginia and Nevada were the only two states to be formed during the Civil War, you know. West Virginia was the only state to form by seceding from a Confederate state. The western region separated from the eastern region and was originally going to be called the State of Kanawha. Ultimately it was just named West Virginia. So Daniel Boone was in the Virginia woods. See?"

Morgan was absolutely dumbstruck and speechless by Earl's logic. He stammered a few times. When he did try to speak, he accidentally swallowed some chewing tobacco. He had been outfoxed and couldn't believe it. Outfoxed by a plowboy. What would be next? Losing more than a game or two of checkers in a week? But as he thought about it, he knew Earl was right. As much as he liked being right most of the time, he knew when he had been licked.

"That is interesting logic. You bested me in that argument, Earl," Morgan said, resigned. "I'll just add one other history fact that you can tell your folks when you write to them tonight. Kanawha was the name of an Indian tribe that lived in West Virginia at one time. I know this because they eventually migrated to Michigan, where I grew up, and joined with the Iroquois Indians."

"Nebraska is actually an Indian word too," Earl said. He was determined to have the last word in this conversation.

"Is that right?" Morgan said.

"The name Nebraska is an Otoe Indian word meaning flat water."

"Flat water, eh?" Morgan repeated.

"That's right," Earl said. He was certain that had to be the last word.

Morgan cleared his throat. That wad of tobacco he'd swallowed wasn't going to do him any favors when they resumed their march. He cleared his throat again. Earl suddenly realized he didn't have the last word.

"You know, Michigan is an Indian word too," Morgan offered.

Earl hadn't expected this. "Huh. Who knew?"

"Michigan is an Ojibwe Indian word meaning large lake," Morgan said.

Earl paused. He would make one last run at having the last word in this conversation.

"Large lake," Earl repeated. This has to be the last word, he thought. Then Morgan swallowed again and cleared his throat.

"Ojibwe," Morgan said, as he scored the last word. He reached into his pack to see what he could find. He found some candy that he had sweet-talked a cute Red Cross volunteer into giving him at the show last evening.

"Share some candy with you, Earl?" he asked.

"Don't mind if I do. Thanks."

"This candy reminds me of the kind my father sold to a grocery store in my home town. Unfortunately he had to close down his candy business," Morgan said.

"What happened?"

"Well, it kinda relates to what we were discussing yesterday when I was whipping you in checkers," Morgan said, as he placed a large pinch of Oliver Twist Fine Cut chewing tobacco in his mouth. He gestured to Earl, offering him some. Earl nodded his head as Morgan continued, "If you have a German background, some people think you're loyal to Germany, not the U.S.A. My father had a side line business of selling his homemade candy and hand butchered meat to the local grocery stores."

"Most farmers need to have another job or another business. They can't just rely on their farm for income," Earl interjected.

"That's right. It doesn't matter whether you farm in Michigan or Nebraska or Virginia," Morgan said, then turned aside to spit. "All of a sudden the grocer decided he didn't need to get his bacon and pork chops from a farmer with the last name of Cook. Someone told the grocer that my grandfather's name was spelled K-O-C-H. Grandfather had changed the name to be spelled C-O-

O-K because Cook was the English way of spelling it. The grocer said he wouldn't do business with anyone that had a German name."

The memory of the incident made Morgan so angry he began talking fast and accidentally swallowed the entire wad of Oliver Twist. His stomach definitely did not approve.

"A neighbor told my father later that it was the grocer's wife who made the decision to stop doing business with him. The grocer's wife figured something wasn't right. She determined this one day when my father brought them some frankfurters. It didn't matter to them that we were Americans now with an English spelled name. They were convinced that we were selling German food to raise money to send to the Kaiser. In a small town, word got out fast. Nobody would buy the candy or meat." Morgan placed his hands over his rumbling stomach.

"Most people now call them hot dogs instead of frankfurters. They're the same thing. Some people just don't use a lick of sense. They'll eat hot dogs but not frankfurters," Morgan said. He took a big gulp from his canteen.

"You can guess the rest. My father wanted me to help him in his meat cutting business, but now there was no business. I no longer had a job, thanks to those so-called neighbors. That is how I ended up at Camp Humphreys—sweating like a pig," Morgan said and then wiped the sweat from his forehead.

The boys were expecting the sergeant to order them back to march at any moment. They continued to sit and talk on the log so as to not give the sergeant any ideas.

"And soon we'll be sweating in a trench in France," Earl added.

"All that trouble over words. I can't figure it out."

"Okay, let's practice our words," Earl said with a grin.

"Sauerkraut. No. Liberty cabbage. Yes."

"German measles. No. Liberty measles. Yes."

"Hamburger. No. Liberty sandwich. Yes."

"What other words do we need to practice?" said Earl.

"Frankfurters. No. Hot dogs. Yes," Morgan added. He gulped more water, hoping it would settle down some of that tobacco lodged in his throat. He briefly remembered his grandfather using chewing tobacco to cure a toothache.

"Why do you chew that stuff?" said Earl. "It seems to be giving you a considerable amount of consternation."

"Well, just remember what General John J. Pershing said: 'You ask me what we need to win this war. I answer tobacco, as much as bullets.'"

"What? Did General Pershing really say that?" Earl was doubtful Morgan knew that bit of information.

"Yes, he did. As sure as you're a plowboy with the rank of private." Morgan had a hay-day with Earl. And if a general can chew tobacco, then I guess I can too."

"Okay, Morgan. I've got a question for you that I'm certain, with the vast and arrayed amount of knowledge in that head of yours, you will know the answer."

Morgan looked at Earl with all the smugness he could muster and thought *of course, I will know the answer. There's not a question Earl can ask me that I won't know the answer to. Or make up a good answer, at least.*

"What is the tallest building in the world?" Earl asked.

"That would be the Eiffel Tower in Paris," Morgan said, with even more smugness than he had previously.

"Right. Now, here's another one," Earl said. "If all the 401st pontoon engineers jumped off the Eiffel Tower, would you jump off too?" Earl was trying hard not to laugh or wiggle his ears.

"Well, I don't know, Earl, but I can tell you that is something my mother would certainly say," Morgan said, then laughed. "There's also a Turkish cigarette called "Murad" that I've noticed is popular. Their advertising slogan is, 'We can do without a lot of things and still win out, you bet. But I'd hate to think of soldiering without a cigarette.'"

Earl still wasn't sure about tobacco because he knew that chewing tobacco caused constant spitting. And he worried it might get stuck in his throat like it did with Morgan. He had to cough and hack to get it out. And cigarettes? The thought of smoking a cigarette seemed worse than chewing tobacco. But Earl was a soldier now. Things were different. He contemplated the thought that if the government issued it in the rations, it couldn't be bad for you. After all, they were headed for trench warfare and mustard gas. That's way worse than some chewing tobacco tucked in your cheek. Earl surmised that at the end of the day, a chew might be just what you need to get you through.

"What's your favorite brand of chewing tobacco, Morgan?"

"Black Cat. But you'll have to settle for some Oliver Twist today," Morgan answered.

"Alright, give me a wad," Earl said, just as the troops were starting to move out to finish their hike. The water break was over.

"A lot of our fellow engineers use chewing tobacco or smoke cigarettes. Just look at the different brands they are getting out. Surely, you've seen the funny poster that advertises a cigarette and says 'Arf a mo Kaiser,'" Morgan said, then laughed.

"Ask the Kaiser to hold the shelling a moment while I light my pipe," Earl said. Both of them were laughing now.

As the soldiers hiked through the steamy woods, Earl was having his first encounter with a chew. And his first experience was, well, an experience. He wasn't sure what to do with it. The wad kept popping out from between his cheek and then he would invariably swallow some. Was that the way it was supposed to work? It had kind of a burning sensation. Trying to figure out chewing tobacco and hiking in formation at the same time was a challenge. He could tell his stomach was objecting to the bits he inadvertently swallowed. And what was this feeling of blood rushing to his head? He became dizzy and a twirling sensation, around and around, wouldn't leave his head. Chewing tobacco was just weird. Maybe this wasn't for him. Or maybe he would try Black Cat next time. Or not take such a large pinch. Some of the boys started to sing "It's a Long Way to Tipperary at mile 16. It was the perfect time for Earl to spit out the chew. He spit it out in a heap and joined in the song, grateful for the excuse.

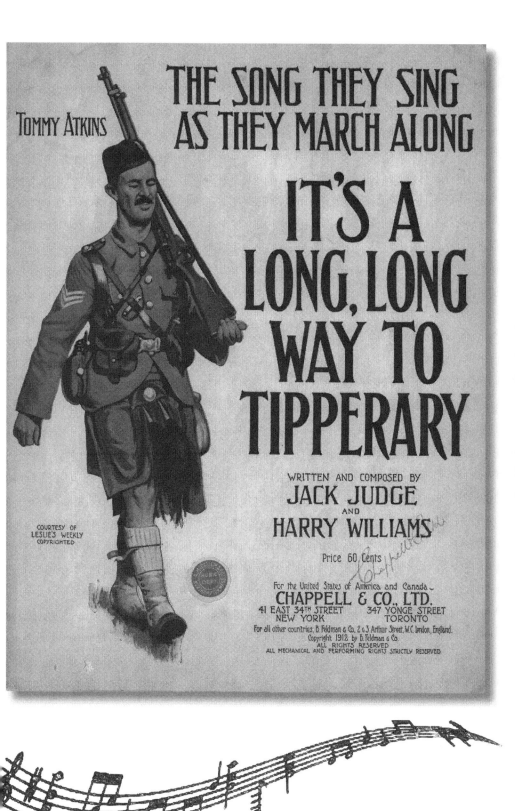

"It's a Long Way to Tipperary"
Song lyrics and music by Jack Judge and Harry Williams, 1912

Up to mighty London, came an Irishman one day.
As the streets are paved with gold, sure everyone was gay;
Singing songs of Piccadilly, Strand & Leicester Square,
Till Paddy got excited, then he shouted to them there.

"It's a long way to Tipperary, it's a long way to go.
It's a long way to Tipperary, to the sweetest girl I know!
Goodbye Piccadilly, Farewell, Leicester Square.
It's a long, long way to Tipperary, but my heart's right there!"

Paddy wrote a letter to his Irish Molly O',
Saying, "Should you not receive it, write and let me know!
If I make mistakes in 'spelling,' Molly dear," said he,
"Remember it's the pen that's bad, don't lay the blame on me."

Molly wrote a neat reply to Irish Paddy O',
Saying, "Mike Maloney wants to marry me, and so,
Leave the Strand and Piccadilly, or you'll be to blame,
For love has fairly drove me silly, hoping you're the same!"

More soldiers collapsed at mile 23. They were so close to being back in camp but couldn't quite make it. Another break was ordered before a last dash to camp, where they shed their packs and got out their canteens. As they sat on a large log, Earl noticed a soldier next to him strike a match on his canteen to light a cigarette. The cigarette packet had a picture of a soldier sitting in the foreground, with a swirl of smoke forming the outline of his sweetheart back home. Thinking of his recent not so great try with chewing tobacco, Earl became curious about cigarettes.

"Could I take a look at that picture on your cigarette pack?" Earl asked the soldier inquisitively.

"Sure. Max McCormick," he said as he held out his hand for a handshake. "The picture is nicely done, eh?" Max took a deep breath, trying to recover from the hike. He seemed to be struggling to catch his breath, drink water, and smoke a cigarette all at the same time. "This picture reminds me of Marie from my home town in Manhattan, New York," he said, as he handed the pack over to Earl.

Earl read aloud the print on one side of the pack: "Bamforths and Company of Holmfirth, England, and New York." He flipped it over and read, Smoke Clouds.

"There's a poem too. Read it out loud. It makes me think of Marie," Max said with a distant look on his face.

Earl read the verse:

Smoke Clouds

I think we are sometimes inclined to forget,
What we owe to the puff of just one cigarette.
It's a wonderful friend to a poor, tired soul,
And it helps one to think life's not bad on the whole.

"Yeah. This one is actually a set of three cards with a different picture and verse on each one," Max informed Earl and placed the cigarette to his lips and inhaled. As the smoke came back out, he coughed a few times and reached into his pack and produced two other pictures.

"These are the other two cards if you want to see them," Max said as he handed them to Earl.

Earl looked at the second card. This one also displayed a picture of a soldier smoking a cigarette, with the smoke forming an image of a woman with her arms around the neck of a soldier.

Earl read its verse:

Smoke Clouds
Smoke Clouds, you sent me dreaming,
Dreaming of bygone days,
As through your filmy haze,
I seem to see the shadow of one long-lost memory;
My heart is nearly breaking,
You are so far away,
But sunshine will follow shadows,
When I come back to you, Love, some day.

Earl suddenly felt like Nebraska was far, far away. The verses made him long for the comfort of home. He felt lonely but was quickly distracted by a burning in his mouth and lips from the Oliver Twist tobacco Morgan gave him. He wasn't sure if that was normal or not and wondered if he shouldn't have taken such a big chew. He bent over to tighten up the laces on his boots. His eyes were drawn to something stuck to the toe of his right boot. He realized that when he spit the whole wad out a few miles back, most of it landed on his boot. He let out a big sigh as he thought about cleaning that off before polishing his boots later.

"I either need to get better at having a chew or give it up," Earl said under his breath.

"What?" Max was still daydreaming of Marie back home.

Earl looked at the picture on the third card. A soldier was smoking and looking into a sunset sky. The smoke made an image of a heart. It moved Earl but he didn't want it to show. He opened his canteen and poured some of the water on his boot to wash off the tobacco, hoping to break up the hardened wad. He took a drink of water and read the verse on the third card:

Smoke Clouds
When you're tired and weary,
Just jogging along,
And you have not a friend,
And the whole world seems wrong.
Only gaze at the smoke clouds,
And never despair,
For there's bound to be
Some silver lining, somewhere.

The voice that caused them much misery ended their water break and conversation. It was the voice of the sergeant. Earl could think of many words to describe him but generally just said he was "sassy" in his letters. The voice gave the order to fall back in line and continue the march.

Oh Lord, that was a short break Earl thought. The soldiers stood up, fell in line, and finished the hike. At least, most of the men finished the hike. Earl may have not had the last word in his conversation with Morgan, but he did march back to camp at a faster pace and beat him by a good 45 minutes. Lesson learned: swallowing tobacco will affect your marching performance.

Earl took advantage of his extra time in the barracks to write.

Pvt. Earl Young
4ᵗʰ E.T.R. Co. C.
Camp A.A. Humphreys, VA
August 28, 1918

Dear Sister & all,

Well, I guess that you are not the only one that was surprised to hear I joined the army.

Yes I joined the army in every sense of the word, but: "by golly" never again for a white man. Some people may like the army or certain parts but this camp is specialized on one thing. Just Engineers. I haven't seen but a few men that wasn't engineers since I arrived here.

It doesn't seem very long but long enough. You wonder why but listen. I enlisted in the quarter Masters Dept. as a dispatch carrier on motorcycle but the army is the army.

The big bugs transfer anyone they stick their finger at, consent or no consent. 50 percent don't get what they enlisted for, so one might just as well be drafted if he don't care for the <u>name</u> of it. Drafted men get the same treatment as a Enlisted man.

I don't remember if I told you what I do here in this god's forsaken wilderness, where "Daniel Boone" used to make a living, or not, but believe me I can tell it because it is drilled into us from 5 a.m. till 10 p.m.

The first week we spent on building Ponton bridges on a little bay down over the hill a mile or so. To do this bridge building is very simple to do but complicated to write down on black & white. Well, it takes about 300 Engineers to do this with any speed & speed is what we want for this work. We usually built just 8 spans or 230 feet with 8 boats or Pontons as they are called. We use the boats for sole support of the bridge, see.

Then, starting at the shore a boat is anchored, both ways. The first stringer are carried out by special duty men. Then the planks are carried by special duty men. Then these stringers are tied a certain way, snugly to the boats. Another boat brought to place, anchored and more lumber carried, not a nail used in a whole bridge. My company made a bridge in less than record time after practicing three or foure mornings.

It took us about 2 hrs. to build the same bridge that we built in 25 minutes & tore down in 12 minutes & every man out of sight. Well, I like that kind of work all O.K. But when it is 110 in the shade one feels mighty limp, bending over a wheel barrow, pick & shovel making a road through the hills & underbrush which exists in the red, sandy, rocky, hard, dry & everything soil here in this newly started camp.

Last January there wasn't a building on the reservation. Now, there is about 30,000 soldiers camped here now & not very many tents either. All wood constructed shacks or barracks. Drop siding & paste board lined. No paint yet. We have single iron cots, two good woolen blankets, a straw tick & a sassy top sergeant.

By the way, I am trying for a Non Commissioned officer, if I produce the goods of which with a little more infantry drill I will, then next highest place is corporal, next sergeant & then Second Lieutenant, first Lieu. and by that time the war will be over. So by the time you hear from me a time or two more I will be wearing "stripes."

The second week we drilled in the a.m. & picked & shoveled the p.m. away the best we knew how.

This is my third week & all drill with guns & bayonets. That bayonet drill kinda runs the shivers up my back once in a while.

How is Draper? Did George get that saddle? How does the machine run. 1100 is pretty good in 6 ½ hours. Keep it up. I am for you but not with you.

The talk here is that the war is nearly over, only if the big bugs would admit it. Oh! Well, I got into it myself and don't blame anyone but the Kaiser. What did Ruth think of my leaving there so sudden. I would like to tell you why I left but don't dare to, see.

Has Paul disposed of Closer yet? I could ask a million questions I suppose but 5 weeks is a long time to be away from everybody you know. I haven't even spoken to a girl in all of these 5 weeks. Several have sung on the stage in the various Y.M.C.A.'s here but nix for mine.

A big shower just came up and also came up the boys on double time. Faster than any have moved since in the army & I "gamble" on it "be it said." Well my arm is awfully sore & tired so had better stop scribbling and take a little snooze before mess. I don't like the cake we get here for there is none. We would have some cake & pie if we had the cake but we don't have any pie. See. Let's see, what did you name or call that cake you used to bake. My, how my mouth waters just at the thought. Maybe you can find time to send one? Pie or cake? Pretty please.

I got your letter last evening with several others from Brock. Nothing looks better than a letter to a sammy. Most of the fellows here are close to home so they can get there over Sunday.

This is long enough so I guess it will serve for you & Millie too so good by & answer soon.

3:37 p.m. Wed. 28th

Earl

P.S. I am laying off today. Took a shot in the arm for typhoid fever this morning and that makes my right arm pain real smart all of the time and is very touchy. It is cloudy & raining a little today. The other fellows are out drilling in the rain.

I get another change of clothes before the week is over. I have worn the same trousers now for 5 weeks without washing. Can you imagine how dirty & greasy they are? You can not! What did you do with my old clothes or did you leave them down to Mr. Harr.

You spoke of Ruth being a very nice girl. Why don't you tell me something I don't realize? Har, Har, Har, Har. Do you ever see any of the other Harr's?

I missed this space so will leave for next time if you bake a nice big cake & some sweet oatmeal cookies.

Excuse poor writing, please.

Answer soon,
Your Brother
Private Earl Young
Camp A.A. Humphrey
Co. C. 4th E.L.R.

My address is different all the time but just write to the last one you know & I will get it. Register the cake for a lot of them that I know of have been lost.

"Are you writing another letter home, Earl?" asked Morgan incredulously.

"No, I'm reading the *Engineer Manual* they gave us," Earl said.

"We get enough of that pontoon bridge stuff during the day. How about some checkers?" Morgan asked.

"Maybe later."

"How about some dominoes then?"

"Maybe later."

"Okay then, how about we get up a game of poker?"

"Maybe later."

"How about—" Morgan started to say.

"Listen to this," Earl interrupted "the *Engineer Manual* in Paragraph 35, Item 2e says that special engineer units are issued equipment designed specifically for the task for which they are organized. Thus, forestry units are equipped with portable sawmills, pontoon units with floating bridge equipage, mapping units with surveying and map reproduction equipment, and water supply units with well-drilling machinery and mobile water purification trucks."

"Huh. So some engineer corps do maps and surveying, eh? All we do is carry heavy equipment to build bridges," Morgan said.

"Yeah. That's why we wear this A.S. patch on our uniforms. Advanced Services," Earl said, as he pointed to the patch on his sleeve.

"Wouldn't you rather carry around a map in the army rather than two hundred pound timbers?" Earl commented.

"I could go for carrying around a map instead of my eleven pound rifle," Morgan said.

"Well, according to the *Engineer Manual* in Paragraph 46, Item b, engineers need to be involved with combat training too. It says engineer troops are armed with a variety of weapons and must be trained to care for their individual and supporting weapons, to be proficient in their use, to know their capabilities and to keep them clean and ready for immediate use at all times."

"Quoting right out of the manual, paragraph and verse, I see," Morgan said.

"You know, you were asking me just the other day, Morgan, why we needed to learn infantry stuff if all we're going to do when we get to France is build bridges."

"And you found the answer in the *Engineer Manual*, I suppose?"

"Yep. Right here. Paragraph 54: The primary mission of the engineer combat battalion is engineer work. However, in an emergency the battalion may be held in mobile reserve and used as infantry in combat. Therefore, tactical training must be conducted in order to meet that emergency. And you were asking the sergeant just yesterday if it was really necessary to take classes on forging," Earl said.

"Yeah, and he about bit my head off too."

"No wonder. I looked it up. The answer to your question is in Paragraph 359, Item b. 'Welding and Forge' section: The foreman of this section is a welder sergeant; he is assisted by other occupational specialists. Fixed equipment includes a welding shop with facilities for both electric-arc and gas welding, and a forge shop consisting of a forging machine, forges, and miscellaneous blacksmith tools and supplies. This section does all welding and forge work for repair of equipment."

"Checkers sounds more interesting to me than that engineer's manual," Morgan said. After pausing for a while, Morgan rubbed his chin like he was thinking really hard. "You know, though, that manual has some interesting stuff in it. Maybe I'll read it. How many pages are there?" Morgan asked.

"Uh, looks like three hundred seven," Earl said, as he paged through to the end of the manual.

"Never mind." Then he cupped his hands to his mouth and yelled across the room: "Who wants to play checkers?"

Morgan found a willing victim and walked away to the other side of the barracks.

"Have a minute, Earl?" a soldier asked, as he walked over to Earl's bunk.

"Sure do. It's Max, right?"

"That's right. You know, I heard you tell someone the other day that the cake in the mess tastes like cordite shrapnel," Max said.

"Yeah. I wasn't complaining as much as I was just missing some of my mother's cooking. Her cakes are especially good and what I miss the most."

"Well, I have just the recipe for you, so to speak." Max grinned. Earl wiggled his ears for Max and wondered if he could really have something to fix his yearning for a really good cake. He hoped Max wasn't kidding.

"My mother found a recipe in the *New York Times* for what is affectionately called Trench Cake," Max said, as he held part of a newspaper in his hand. "She sent me both the recipe and an honest to goodness Trench Cake. I'm willing to share it with you because I can't eat the entire thing all by myself. First, I'll read the recipe to you. Just so you'll know what's in it. Then you can have a big slice. If you're still interested, that is. I'd hate to have you eat a piece of my mom's cake just to be polite."

"I'm sure I'll like it, Max. Just hurry up and read that recipe if you must, so we can get to the eating part," Earl pleaded.

Max read off the main ingredients but was happy to let Earl borrow it to copy for his mother.

Trench Cake

Ingredients
- 2/3 cup plain flour
- 3/8 cup butter
- ¼ cup brown sugar
- ¼ cup currants/raisins
- ¼ pint milk
- 1 teaspoon vinegar
- 2 teaspoon cocoa powder
- ½ teaspoon bicarb of soda
- ½ teaspoon ground nutmeg
- ½ teaspoon ginger
- 2 tablespoon lemon rind

Instructions
- Preheat oven to 350F. Grease and line an 8-inch cake tin.
- Rub together the butter and flour.
- Add the rest of the ingredients, except for the bicarb of soda.
- Mix together the milk, vinegar, and bicarb.
- Add to the bowl and mix well.
- Pour into the tin and bake for 75 minutes.
- Remove from tin when slightly cooled.
- Allow cake to completely cool.

"That's the recipe. Before I give you a piece of cake to try, I have to also read what my mom wrote about it: This is a dense cake and heavy. Although it looks like it could be used as a British eighteen pounder cannonball, do not be deceived. It is delicious and bound to satisfy," Max said.

"Not to worry, Max," Earl said then he licked his lips, his mouth drooling for a bite. "If we're headed for the trenches and if I can endure trench checkers with Morgan on an almost daily basis, then I most certainly should have a piece of that trench cake."

9

The Lily

"Somewhere in France Is the Lily"
Song lyrics by Philander Johnson, music by Joseph E. Howard; 1917

One day as morning shed its glow,
Across the eastern sky,
A boy and girl in accents low,
In a garden said "Goodbye!"
She said, "Remember as you stray,
When each must do his share,
The flowers blooming here today
Are emblems over there!"

Somewhere in France is the Lily,
Close by the English Rose;
A thistle so keen, and a Shamrock green,
And each loyal flow'r that grows.
Somewhere in France is a sweetheart,
Facing the battle's chance.
For the flow'r of our youth fights for freedom and truth,
Somewhere in France.

Each morning in that garden fair,
Where sweetest perfumes dwell,
The lassie whispers low a pray'r,
For the flowers she loves so well.
And over there as night draws near,
Amid the shot and flame,
Unto the flag he holds so dear,
A soldier breathes her name.

Earl woke up hungry. For some reason he had not slept well. He dreamed about getting boxes of oatmeal cookies, pumpkin pies, and plum pudding. Hopefully his family would send him cookies or something in the mail. He had also awakened to the thought of Ruth Harr. She was his age and always smelled like lavender. She was polite and spoke to Earl whenever their family would get together. Ruth's parents and Earl's brother, George, and George's wife, Laura, were neighbors and helped each other out, especially during the summer, and even more so when it was threshing bee time. It was great to be able to call on someone when something broke and you just needed that extra hand. That way you could fix what was broken and get back to work. That's just the way things were.

He remembered one Sunday picnic that took place in Mud Springs—an old pony express station northwest of Dalton. People would gather there on weekends to soak their feet in the creek and enjoy each other's company. Earl thought about how Ruth had cut an extra-large piece of lemon pound cake and had given it to him. They sat by the creek together, eating their cake. Both families kept looking at them. They all seemed to have these silly and awkward expressions on their faces. It made Earl feel a little self-conscious and yet, he liked being with Ruth and talking with her. He didn't get the chance that often. And Ruth seemed to be interested in him.

On the way home that day, he rode with George and Laura.

"I saw that you and Ruth seemed to hit it off real well, Earl," said Laura.

"Yeah. She makes good cake," Earl said. He felt his face getting warm.

"Well, she sure is a nice girl, even if you just like her for her cake," Laura said then smirked. "You be sure you're nice to her, Earl."

"I wouldn't think of anything else, that's for certain. Do you think we'll have another picnic with the Harr's again, soon?"

"Well, if the Lord's willing and the creek don't rise," Laura said in a teasing way.

Thoughts of the picnic and Ruth swirled in Earl's head into that evening: the next day, after the picnic, George, Earl, and Laura had arrived at noon to help a neighbor with their farming. Five other families had also gathered at the Double T Ranch. Mr. Thurman, the owner, had broken his leg and it was time to take a cutting of hay out of the fields and into the barn. While the men loaded huge piles of hay onto their wagons, the women helped Mrs. Thurman with a quilt. At the end of the day everyone gathered in the barn to listen to a representative from the Nebraska state legislature. His name was Lewis Brott, who also was a farmer in Cheyenne County. His farm was several miles north of a town called Potter, in a district called Sextorp. Earl was glad that he didn't live in that district. He couldn't imagine having to explain he was from Sextorp.

Senator Brott talked briefly to the crowd about his experimentation in growing and cultivating alfalfa on the high plains by planting it in rows. But, for the most part, he gave the families the latest information on the fighting in France. Senator Brott was formerly a Republican but changed parties and was now a Democrat. He enjoyed being a Democrat, particularly since President Woodrow Wilson was a member of that same political party. He then introduced Eleanor Weber, who was there for two reasons: One, she was a member of the NWP, the National Woman's Party, and was speaking in favor of adopting a nineteenth amendment to the U.S. Constitution. This would give women the right to vote. And two, she was there because of her excellent singing voice.

Eleanor's song had stirred feelings deep down in Earl. He tried to understand what was causing them to bubble up, then his thoughts drifted back to the picnic that had been so enjoyable. Earl remembered laughing and enjoying apple pie, lemon pound cake, ice cream, and the company of a pretty girl. He listened closely as Eleanor's voice reverberated in the barn. Now, his mind was drifting to France where a war raged and young men were fighting and dying for the very freedoms Earl experienced every day. The song was stirring something in him he hadn't yet experienced: He knew it was time to help ensure those freedoms. But he just wasn't sure how.

Earl's warm memories of his time at home in western Nebraska filled him up for the day of army life ahead. The picnic, now, seemed like a long time ago but it was only a few weeks ago. Maybe he could add another W to Laura's Ws: wheat, war—and women. As he was learning the ways of the army, life continued in Dalton, Nebraska. Laura was eight months pregnant with her first child. Naturally, the child would be born on the farm. Dr. Taylor in Sidney would be called only if absolutely necessary.

Laura asked Earl's sister, Millie, to come out from eastern Nebraska to help deliver the baby. Millie was happy to accommodate and expected to stay a week or two. Laura's baby was due any day, and she still worked 16-hour days. She was grateful Millie was there to help cook and feed as many as 15 hungry men several meals each day. The county schoolteacher stayed with them too.

In a few weeks, Laura had given birth and was adjusting to life as a new mother, while Millie stayed on for a month or two more to help feed all the farmers. Even though Millie and her parents were both in Nebraska, the two towns of Dalton and Brock were 450 miles apart. Like her brother, Millie also wrote letters home.

Millie Young.
Earl's suitcase collection.

Millie Young
40 geo young
Dalton Nebr.

Mrs. Joseph Young
Brock, Nebraska
R. F. D. Box 40.

Mon. A. M. Its misting heavy nearly hard enough to rain so we arn't washing.

I would like to have a pint bottle of Special Pink along with my things. I ordered medicine number 29885 from Hardin but the bottle was broke and had all leaked out so maybe if you tell him about it he will send another bottle. He ought to anyhow. I guess some of my winter things are in that big trunk in the west room.

Millie Young
c/o Geo. L Young
Dalton, Nebraska
Sept 1ˢᵗ, 1918

Dear Folks at home,

Rec'd your little letter yesterday and tho't I'd try to do as well. We spent the last 5 days cooking for 15 men for dinner and 12 for supper & breakfast besides Paul, Wiellie & Dewey. Tomorrow they thresh for another farmer and they will board the men there. After that job we board them again 3 or 4 days. They go back & forth to the machine in cars for meals. Paul finished plowing for George then disked it and now he has the tractor and disk and drill on behind drilling in his own wheat. He takes his dinner with him.

Tomorrow school starts and the school mam boards here to start with at least.

Laura and I was wishing we had a bunch of those nice grapes but guess that's out of the question this year. Laura wants me to stay with her for a while. Maybe till Dec. And I want my clothes.

Never heard from Earl this wk. If there is any mail come there for me please forward it. Ed was over a minute Friday a.m. and was looking for a cook. Nothing doing. He said the wind we had Thurs. eve. blew his shack over. The supper was all ready & table set. They simply took the scoop and heaved it out. Broke all the dishes but 2 boals. It didn't seem such a bad storm but he didn't have it braced.

Must close now got a two weeks washing on for tomorrow but the engine does the scrubbing. Went to Sidney this afternoon. Geo. got some work done on his car. The key to my trunk is in that handkerchief box on the bureau if not <u>somewheres close.</u> I want my *good gingham dresses and shoes, heavy stockings & coat and such things that come handy and my princes slip pattern in the dresser drawer downstairs. Overshoes, everyday coat, hood and sweater and overshoes.*

Put in some of those coat & skirt hangers too. I don't know of anything else just now I might need. Those things that are in the top of my trunk put in a safe, mouse proof non destructable place for safe keeping. The key had better be sent by mail and maybe you better rope the trunk good so it gets here whole. Be sure to write when you send it so we can look for it.

You ought to see the corn out here this year. It's tall and got good big ears. One piece near Sidney was nearly ripe already. Too dry for it I guess. Haven't had rain since wk ago Tuesday nearly two weeks now.

Ans. often. Bye Bye,
Millie

P.S. Mon. a.m. It's misting heavy nearly hard enough to rain so we aren't washing. I would like to have a pint bottle of Special Pink along with my things. I ordered medicine number 29885 from Hardin but the bottle was broke and had all leaked out so maybe if you tell him about it he will send another bottle. He ought to anyhow. I guess some of my winter things are in that big trunk in the west room.

· · ·

Earl, Morgan, and the other soldiers had an exhausting week. They were up at 5:00 a.m. and didn't finish until 10:00 p.m. every day. By the time the troops fell into their iron cots, they were asleep before the blankets warmed up over them. Saturday, though, had been a day when things finished up early and the boys could play checkers to pass the time.

After a few moves and a few jumps, the board that Morgan and Earl were playing on had an equal number of red and black pieces.

"What's the news from home, Earl?" Morgan asked.

"Got a newspaper sent to me," Earl replied. "When I was grow-ing up in Brock, I always liked to read the *Auburn Newspaper*. It's a real treat that my folks sent one to me a few days ago."

"Anything interesting?" Morgan inquired.

"There was, actually. It was disturbing and had to do with what we were talking about the other day. Everyone is getting afraid of anything German," Earl said.

"What was the story about?"

"A group of farmers in Missouri—got really riled up. One of the farmers had an unusual kind of a dog that looked like a wolf. He called it a German Shephard. So those farmers gathered up their rifles one day, chased that dog into the woods and . . . they shot it. Just because it was a "German" Shephard. Can you believe that?"

"To kill a dog!" Morgan had both hands up on top of his head. "Did you hear the story that Isaac told yesterday?" Morgan asked Earl.

"You mean Isaac from New York? What story?"

"His mother works at a library in his hometown in New York. A few weeks ago somebody found some books written in German and—" Morgan got cut off.

"Oh, don't tell me," Earl interrupted, concerned what Morgan was going to say next.

"Yep, they gathered up all those books with anything that even sounded German. They started a big fire in the middle of the street and burned anything to do with Germany. Even some geography books," Morgan continued. "And if that isn't bad enough, they started to get rough with Isaac's mother because they figured anyone hiding German books in a building had to be a German loyalist."

"What did they do to her?" Earl asked, unbelievably.

"They slapped her around a little bit. Threatened to throw her on the fire too. Scared the wits out of her," Morgan said.

They were silent for a minute.

"In Nebraska people can't sing songs in church in German anymore either," Earl said.

"That's happened in a number of states," Morgan added. "Never mind that you're in church to get guidance to help your fellow man."

"Right. It brings into question your loyalty—Germany or U.S.A.?" Earl said.

"I can't sing a song to save my soul. In my opinion any American should be able to sing a song in German without their loyalty being questioned," Morgan said.

"I agree. My parents came over from Germany, and their English may not be the best but they try," Earl said. "And they made sure that their children went to school and learned reading, writing, and arithmetic. In English."

Morgan thought for a bit then asked, "Is arithmetic different in English than it is in German? I mean, if you add two plus two in German, do you still get four?"

"Well, I may be just a plowboy but I think they get the same answer," Earl said then smiled. "Nebraska even passed a law in their legislature that church services in the state could not be spoken in German anymore," Earl said.

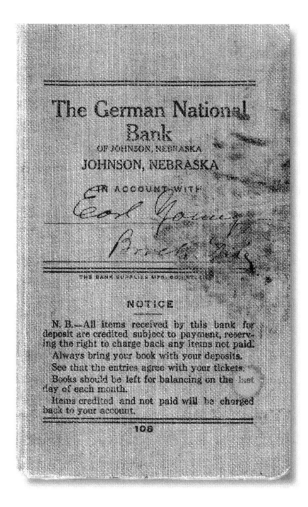

Earl's suitcase collection. Earl Young's bank book. Account with German National Bank in Johnson, Nebraska. Last balance listed on March 27, 1917, for $6.89.

"That must be kind of hard on churches like the German-Lutheran church I grew up in," Morgan said.

"The songs, the words, the sermon—everything has to be in English," Earl continued. "People speak in German in church just because it's familiar. It's what they are used to. Not because they like the Kaiser."

Earl spotted a Lutheran hymnal and when he thumbed through the book, the page that the hymnal opened to was the song titled "A Mighty Fortress Is Our God." He also read that the hymn was a reflection on Psalm 46. He thought it would be interesting to compare the words of the Psalm to the hymn that Martin Luther composed.

"Psalm 46:1-3"
God is our refuge and strength, a very present help in trouble,
Therefore we will not fear though the earth should change,
Though the mountains shake in the heart of the sea;
Though its waters roar and foam,
Though the mountains tremble with its tumult.

"Some of our Lutheran church service in Michigan was in German," Morgan said. "We used to sing a lot of songs in German too." Morgan looked around cautiously to make sure no one else was listening.

He stood up close to Earl and quietly said, "Ein Feste Burg Ist Unser Gott," then moved back to his chair. "That's German for the hymn 'A Mighty Fortress Is Our God' and the extent of my German language. My parents never taught me. They thought that since we lived in America now, I didn't need a language other than English. The church we attended sang their hymns in German, so I picked up a few words," Morgan said.

He paused for a moment of reflection. "There was one other disadvantage about the sermon *not* being in German all the time," Morgan chuckled.

"What's that?"

"I went to church once where the minister spoke German the entire time. He talked for over an hour. It was the best nap I ever had."

"A Mighty Fortress Is Our God"
Hymn lyrics by Martin Luther's "Ein feste Burg ist unser Gott,"
1529; translated in English by Frederick Hedge, 1853,

A mighty Fortress is our God,
A bulwark never failing;
Our helper He, amid the flood
Of mortal ills prevailing.
For still our ancient foe
Doth seek to work his woe;
His craft and power are great,
And armed with cruel hate,
On earth is not his equal.

Did we in our own strength confide,
Our striving would be losing,
Were not the right Man on our side,
The Man of God's own choosing.
Dost ask who that may be?
Christ Jesus, it is He;
Lord Sabaoth is His name,
From age to age the same;
and He must win the battle.

And though this world, with devils filled,
Should threaten to undo us,
We will not fear, for God has willed
His truth to triumph through us.
The Prince of Darkness grim,
We tremble not for him;
His rage we can endure,
For lo! his doom is sure;
One little word shall fell him.

That word above all earthly powers—
No thanks to them—abideth;
The Spirit and the gifts are ours
Through Him who with us sideth.
Let goods and kindred go,
This mortal life also:
The body they may kill:
God's truth abideth still,
His kingdom is forever!

Earl thought about the song. He liked that hymn. It was one of his favorites. He remembered the many times being in church he sang a hymn called "From Heaven Above to Earth I Come." He mostly remembered it because of its many verses. Lutherans usually sang the entire song, no matter how long the service. Every verse. His legs would get tired singing all 15 verses of the same song. He really liked "The Old Rugged Cross," but it was a new hymn and he had only heard it once.

He thought about how hymns ended by singing the word "Amen." It was interesting to him that hymns that were sung in English ended by singing "Amen." And when hymns were sung in German, they also ended by singing the exact same word. "Amen."

Now Earl was trying to reconcile the meaning of German words and English words in his head. Some church people were very anti-German. They didn't like the German language being spoken anywhere. No way, no how. They didn't like even single, solitary German words being spoken. What sense did it make that the same anti-Germans could end their hymns by singing loudly and clearly a very German word: "Amen"?

Earl opened the Lutheran hymnal to read "From Heaven Above to Earth I Come." There were *all* 15 verses. He chuckled just think-ing about a guy in church expecting to leave soon and then hearing the pastor say they'd be singing *all* the verses.

"From Heaven Above to Earth I Come"
A hymn by Martin Luther's "Vom Himmel hoch, da komm' ich
her," 1535; translated in English by Catherin Winkwork

From heaven above to earth I come,
To bear good news to ev'ry home;
Glad tidings of great joy I bring,
Whereof I now will say and sing:

To you, this night, is born a Child
Of Mary, chosen mother mild;
This tender Child, of lowly birth,
Shall be the joy of all the earth.

'Tis Christ, our God, who far on high,
Had heard your sad and bitter cry;
Himself will your salvation be,
Himself from sin will make you free.

Now let us all with gladsome cheer,
Follow the shepherds, and draw near
To see the wondrous Gift of God,
Who hath His own dear Son bestowed.

Glory to God in highest heav'n,
Who unto us His Son has giv'n.
While angels sing, with pious mirth,
A glad New Year to all the earth.

Earl smiled as he finished reading the last verse. The Methodists would sing verses one and two and call it good. But the Lutherans? All 15 verses. Guaranteed.

Another day. It was September now. The Virginia weather was cooling off and the boys had extra coffee for breakfast to warm up.

"Those biscuits and gravy hit the spot this morning," Morgan said, as he patted his stomach.

"Indeed they did," Earl replied. "Time for another cup?"

"You betcha."

They picked up their conversation of the evening before, just as if they hadn't slept seven hours in between. Truth be told, it was their way of staving off the nervousness of not knowing what was coming next. Morgan started things up again.

"I heard a lot of people in my community, non-Germans, say if you want to talk German and sing in German and pray in German then just move back to Germany."

"That's ridiculous," Earl said. "People who moved here from Germany came here because they wanted to be here. I couldn't stop thinking about it as I was laying in my cot, trying to fall sleep last night. My parents left Germany partly because the German government was forcing young men into military service. They left Germany so I and my brothers wouldn't have to go to war and fight."

"Ironic isn't it? My parents, Joseph and Elizabeth Young, left to avoid the exact circumstance we're in now. Germany was pressing their young men into a war. In order to protect their sons, they left. And what now? Now we are even fighting against the country they left."

"Well, some of us have to join the army. One, to show people that we may have a German heritage but we are in this fight to stop Germany. Two, to get rid of the Kaiser who wants to destroy freedom and take over all of Europe," Morgan said then took a big, hot sip of coffee.

"Hopefully some of these anti-German feelings will settle down when people know that boys like you and me, whose families changed their names from Jung to Young and Koch to Cook, have joined the army and training to fight," Earl said.

"So let's go get some training in," Morgan said, as he slapped Earl on the back.

"Let's do it. We enlisted to take a little trip to France. I want to learn what the army wants me to do when I get there. I'm ready to go today," Earl said with a determined look.

The sergeant of their unit was ready to oblige. They got more training in Pontoon bridge building that day. There was a lot of talk among the boys that they would soon be saying "Au Revoir" to A. A. Camp Humphreys. That evening, Earl's hard work during the day was rewarded by what he received in the mail.

I counted up a while ago just how many different states I have seen. They are Nebraska, Colorado, Wyoming, Kansas, Iowa, Missouri, Illinois, Indiana, Kentucky, West Virginia, Virginia, & Maryland. I expect to see North Carolina, South Carolina, & Georgia before very many more, [because] we will be three miles from the Tennessee line

I have a pocket [...] me so I can [...] all the time. See, [...] get there & [...] I will write [...] about it & more [...]

hello & be good.

Loving lips,

Earl.

ARMY AND NAVY
YOUNG MEN'S CHRISTIAN ASSOCIATION
"WITH THE COLORS"

YMCA

A. A. Humphreys
Virginia.

Dear Mother.

I received the most welcomed present yesterday that I ever received in all my life. I feel that I can never be able to thank you enough for them grapes, for they certainly were fine. Only a handfull in the whole basket were spoiled or smashed. They were certainly fine. I treated about a dozen of the boys that sleep next to me, as they treat when they get some cake or candy or cigars as it may be.

Another treat is comming to 12 of us from this company today. We are leaving here for camp Forest, Georgia to day some time.

A. Humphreys
Virginia

Dear Mother,

    I received the most welcomed present yesterday that I ever received in all my life. I feel that I can never be able to thank you enough for them grapes, for they certainly were fine. Only a handful in the whole basket were spoiled or smashed. They were certainly fine. I treated about a dozen of the boys that sleep next to me, as they treat when they get some cake or candy or cigars as it may be.

    Another treat is coming to 12 of us from this company today. We are leaving here for Camp Forest, Georgia today some time. Some of the fellows say that they seldom keep soldiers there for more than 2 weeks before they go across the "pond". One can't believe everything he hears around here tho.

    I enlisted for that little trip and every soldier looks forward to the day they start for France. I don't look for the war to last much longer tho any-way. The Engineers don't see the front line trenches very much so don't worry about me for I have learned my gun pretty good. We had some practice shooting yesterday & received compliments from the Captain that I was one of the best shooters. Shooting 5 times in 25 seconds & hitting the bulls eye 3 out of 5 & coming close enough to get a Hun the other two isn't bad at all. Some can't hit the target board even.

    Well, whatever takes place I always strain every muscle to do it right. The muscles of my legs or in fact every muscle is just as hard as grissle. I used to fag out when it comes to a couple miles walking but now we get out & drill 130 steps a minute for 6 or 7 hrs. a day as regular as the day comes around and hardly feel tired at night. Just try that little stunt once when you go after the mail or something. See.

The top sergeant just called for me to come to help take a sick man to the housepital. He belched, puked & cried all the way up there then when we got there the doctor gave him an awful bawling out for ever coming up there when he wasn't sick. The poor fellow had to come back & go to bed with just the sympathy that us privates could give him. That doctor don't know beans. I got some pills for my cold the other morning, but they couldn't even make them work.

I counted up a while ago just how many different states I have seen. They are Nebraska, Colorado, Wyoming, Kansas, Iowa, Missouri, Illinois, Indiana, Kentucky, West Virginia, Virginia & Maryland. I expect to see North Carolina, South Caroling & Georgia before very many hours to pass. We will be three miles from the Tennessee line at Camp Forest. I have a pocket U.S.A. map with me so I can tell just where I am all the time. See.

Well when I get there & get a new address I will write and tell you all about it & more too if possible.

Tell all hello & be good.
Your Sammy boy,
Earl

The following morning, most of the soldiers at Camp A. A. Humphreys got their orders to board a train. Most were excited to be one step closer to taking the fight to the Kaiser and Earl worked hard to be one of the best, be the fight in Berlin or somewhere in France, it didn't matter. He would do whatever was needed. He would build pontoon bridges, shoot his rifle, dig trenches. His hard work was rewarded as he and eight other soldiers were selected from their regiment of 200 for the next step in training.

The 401st Pontoon Engineers were getting closer to going overseas. Earl was proud and ready to be sent to France. He knew his mother worried about him, so he took time to write one last letter to her from Camp Humphreys before leaving for his new assignment at Camp Forrest.

Earl signed his letters in different ways. Sometimes just plain ole *Earl*. Sometimes *your sonny boy*. Sometimes *your son*. Today he was feeling what the British would call tickety-boo and signed the letter *Your Sammy Boy*. When he addressed the next letter to his mother, he smiled as he thought about her reaction at his signing the name *Sammy*. The name Sammy was a spin-off of Uncle Sam, the iconic symbol of the U.S.A. Sammy was a word he had heard recently on a march, a word the British used to refer to the American doughboys; sometimes, in the same way they would use the word Yanks.

10

Your Sammy Boy

"So Long Sammy"
Song lyrics by Benny Davis and Jack Yellen,
music by Albert Gumble; 1917

We're mighty proud of you, Sammy boy.
You've proved that you are true, Sammy boy.
Though the time has come to part,
There's something in my heart
That seems to turn the sadness into joy;
We're sorry that you have to go,
But you won't be gone for long I know.

So long, Sammy! May good luck be in your guide;
You've fill'd your dear old mammy's heart with pride.
Keep smiling Sammy.
Go and show what you can do;
We love you, Sammy boy!
Goodbye and good luck to you!

While you are over there, Sammy boy,
We know you'll do your share, Sammy boy.
There are many wrongs to right,

That's why we're in the fight,
So fight with all your might, our Sammy boy.
A hundred million hearts will pray,
For our faithful Sammy every day.

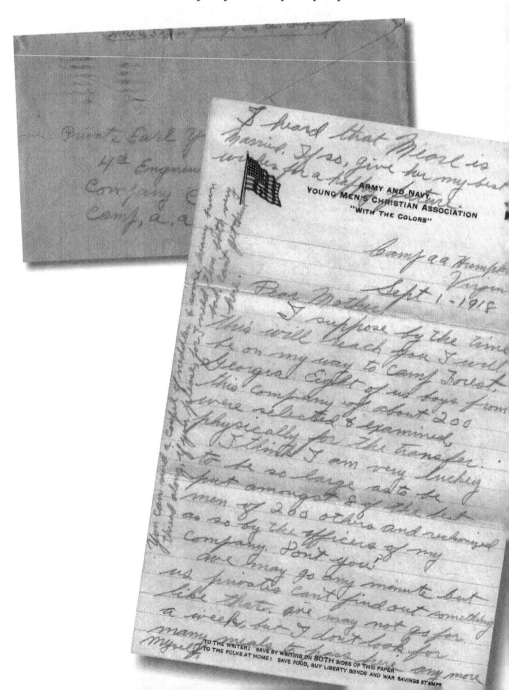

Private Earl Young
4th Engineering Training Regiment
Company C
Camp A.A. Humphreys
Sept. 1, 1918

Dear Mother,

I suppose by the time this will reach you I will be on my way to Camp Forest, Georgia. Eight of us boys from this company of about 200 were selected & examined, physically for the transfer. I think I am very lucky to be so large as to be put amongst 8 of the best men of 200 others and recognized as so by the officers of my company. Don't you! We may go any minute but us privates can't find out something like that. We may not go for a week, but I don't look for many meals to pass here anymore myself.

I go on Guard Duty at 4 p.m. today for a period of 24 hrs. 4 hrs. guard duty then 2 hrs. rest & exchange with the rest of the fellows in turn. See. We are put out with a certain place to guard with unloaded gun & bayonet attached to end of gun for protection against enemies.

Yesterday was inspection day. They inspect our clothes & guns. Not a speck of dirt or grease is allowed, even ever so small is allowed. If everything is spick & span the Lieutenant says "very good." If dirty he takes the name & puts it on the "Black List". That means we go on kitchen duty for a week or any dirty work to be done around here. I got very good but didn't expect it. I was so nervous I couldn't hardly hand him the gun in the correct manner. I think they caught about 30 dirty guns on that inspection. It takes nearly all spare time scrubbing & petting that pesky gun, I call it that but regard it as my best friend I have in the army.

Really we had a pretty good dinner today. Smashed potatoes without butter or cream, greasy, sloppy gravey, good white bread, sour watter, supposed to be lemonade but I know there wasn't half enough lemons & no sugar in it. Some kind of fruit, peaches & pears & tomatoes mixed I guess, good tho to a hungry man. We had a little tough pork & some corn too.

The weather was pretty sultry here until the last few days and nights especially. I have three blankets now, something like horse blankets, you know, but they failed their full duty last night, so you see it got real chilly by morning.

I take a shower bath nearly every other night and that watter is just as it is pumped from the Potomac river. It takes lots of ambition to get under that cold stream of watter long enough for a bath. We must shave every day.

I get along fine now with my drill work & have worked to the front of my squad. Write often.

Your Sammy boy,
Earl

> *Just write the new address and it will be forwarded if I move.*
> *4th E.T.R. Co. C*
> *A.A. Humphreys,*
> *Virginia*

> *P.S. I heard that Meorl is married. If so, give her my best wishes for a happy future.*
> *You can send a couple of needles & some heavy brown thread along, if you please, for I need them both very bad. Can't get them here.*
> *Got a letter from Mabel & one from Robert Massey yesterday.*

Earl enjoyed 42 hours on the train. It gave him time to see states, which previously was something he only saw in books. He enjoyed the adventure the army was giving him. The troop train moved slowly, and he was able to compare differences in farms they passed to those in Nebraska. Crops were different too. Tobacco fields. Cotton. He didn't see anything that made him want to grow anything other than wheat. Satisfied with his new discoveries, he pulled out his writing material from his satchel.

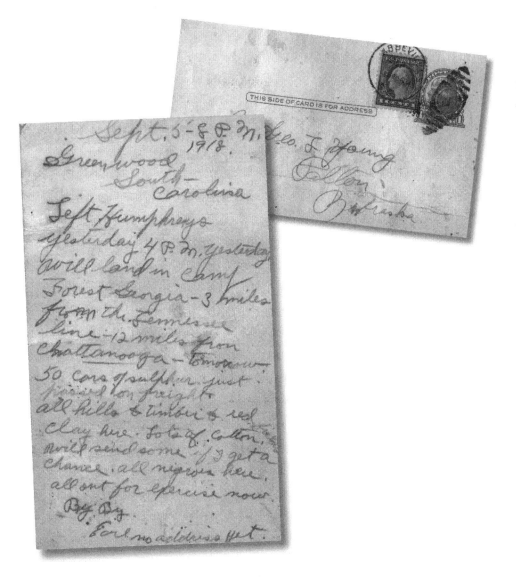

Mr. Geo. L. Young
Dalton, Nebraska
Sept. 5 -1918, 8 p.m.
Greenwood, South Carolina

Left Humphreys yesterday 4 pm yesterday. Will land in Camp Forest, Georgia—3 miles from the Tennessee line—12 miles from Chattanooga—tomorrow.

50 cars of sulphur just passed on freight. All hills & timber & red clay here. Lots of cotton.

Will send some if I get a chance. All negro's here. All out for exercise now.

By By
Earl
No address yet

It seemed strange to him that he'd be in Georgia. He hadn't thought too much about visiting when he daydreamed about seeing other states. He stood up to stretch and noticed a newspaper in one of the seats. It was the *Atlanta Georgian*.

Earl found a comfortable position and opened the crisp paper. It was quite informative: The state of Georgia was home to more training camps than any other state, and each camp trained soldiers for various specialties. Some camps were mostly for infantry. Some, tank or air support. Some were oriented for equipment or pontoon bridges. The article stated the doughboys traveled by ship to Germany and France to fight the Huns. *The doughboys—that's our nickname* thought Earl. He read on. The term doughboys was used to describe soldiers in the American Expeditionary Force: Soldiers stationed overseas enjoyed fried flour dumplings called doughboys. Meals in the field were often doughy flour, formed around a bayonet, and cooked over campfire flames. Earl was proud to be a certified doughboy.

He read on, learning a lot about his own venture. Another article discussed a nasty outbreak of the Spanish flu at a training camp called Camp Hancock near Augusta, Georgia. The number of soldiers who contracted influenza jumped from two to 716 in just two hours. He had heard reports that this flu was extremely contagious and was relieved his orders took him to Camp Forrest instead.

There was also a poem reprinted in the paper:

"For the Fallen"
A poem by Robert Laurence Binyon, 1914

With proud thanksgiving, a mother for her children,
England mourns for her dead across the sea.
Flesh of her flesh they were, spirit of her spirit,
Fallen in the cause of the free.

Solemn the drums thrill; Death august and royal
Sings sorrow up into immortal spheres,
There is music in the midst of desolation
And a glory that shines upon our tears.

They went with songs to the battle, they were young,
Straight of limb, true of eye, steady and aglow.
They were staunch to the end against odds uncounted;
They fell with their faces to the foe.

They shall not grow old, as we that are left grow old:
Age shall not weary them, nor the years contemn.
At the going down of the sun and in the morning,
We will remember them.

They mingle not with their laughing comrades again;
They sit no more at familiar tables of home;
They have no lot in our labour of the day-time;
They sleep beyond England's foam.

But where our desires are and our hopes profound,
Felt as a well-spring that is hidden from sight,
To the innermost heart of their own land they are known,
As the stars are known to the Night;

As the stars that shall be bright when we are dust,
Moving in marches upon the heavenly plain;
As the stars that are starry in the time of our darkness,
To the end, to the end, they remain.

It was written a few weeks after the British Expeditionary Force had suffered heavy casualties. The war had just been in the first weeks of hostilities and the British made the decision to 'stand and fight' the Imperial German Army at the Battle of Le Cateau. The poem struck a note with Earl and he knew he'd always remember it.

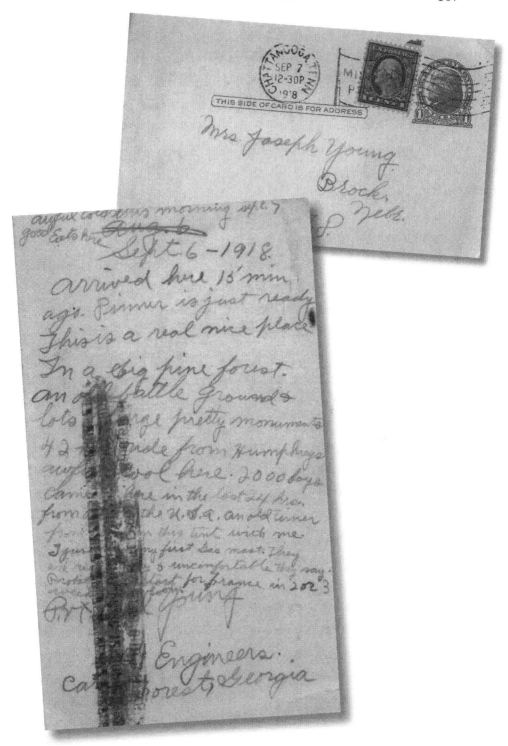

awful cold this morning sept 7
good Eats here ~~thugh~~

Sept. 6 - 1918.
arrived here 15 min
ago. Dinner is just ready
This is a real nice place
In a big pine forest.
an old battle ground
lots large pretty monuments
42 mile from Humphrys
aught cool here. 2000 boys
came here in the last 24 hrs.
from all over the U.S.A. an old timer
from ____ in this tent with me.
I gut my first Gas mask. They
ah reel ____ s uncomfortable they say.
Protb____ ____ fact for France in 2 or 3
____ ____ ____ young

___ ___ Engineers.
ca___ ___orest, Georgia

Mrs. Joseph Young
Brock, Nebr.
R.F.D.
Sept 6, 1918

  Arrived here 15 min. ago. Dinner is just ready.
  This is a real nice place. In a big pine forest.
  An old battleground & lots of large pretty monuments. 42 hrs.
ride from Humphreys.
  Awfully cool here. 2000 boys came in here in the last 24 hrs.
from all over the U.S.A. An old timer from Ten. shared his tent
with me.
  I just got my first gas mask today. They are hot &
uncomfortable.
  They say probably headed for France in 2 or 3 weeks.

Pvt. Earl Young
Army Engineers
Camp Forest, Georgia

  Awful cold this morning Sept. 7.
  Good eats here.

Private Earl Young
401 Ponton Park
Camp Forest, Georgia
Sept. 8, 1918

Dear Brother,

I haven't received any mail from you for a long time so will write a line or two to let you know where I am. Lots of the mail gets lost beings there so much transferring going on these days. I don't just understand what these transfers mean but our Captain told us that we wouldn't be here in Georgia more than two weeks, possibly not that long. Said we would be going back to New Jersey or New York for a day or two & then across the "pond" where we get 2 months real training. That sounds good to the whole bunch of 200 of us.

We are just 5 miles northeast of Chattanooga, Tennessee. Believe me I have been over some ground in the last six weeks. I wish you could have been along with me. I have been through some 15 or 16 states. This little pocket map I have sure comes in handy.

Say you ought to see this camp where I am now. It used to be an old battleground of the Civil War. Lots of monuments around here worth looking at, believe me. Cedar trees here 3 feet in diameter & 100 feet high. Lots of trees here. I don't know the names of. The last days ride we saw nothing but small cotton fields & cornfields on the sides of the red clay, baby-mountains. The corn beats Cheyenne Co. a little bit & I don't think much of the cotton.

Say, you ought to see the rifles we get now. They are issuing us all new ones this morning. They have been dipped with some kind of thick grease before they are packed. It takes about 4 hours to get one clean. I cleaned two all ready but had to leave both of them at Humphreys. The one we get now we take across the water with us.

When does Edw. expect to be drafted. He never writes, so write for him.

How did you come out on the threshing deal this year.

Must go and get my greasy old "Friend" now. Will send you some pictures if I can get a hold of some film here. We get better eats here than at Humphreys. Really we got some sugar in the black coffee this morning. Some fried potatoes, white bread & the first slice of fried ham in five weeks. Fresh biscuits too this morning. Sounds good, but listen this is Sunday. We got breakfast at 9:30 this morning.

It is awful cool here, close to the mountains you know. Half of the fellows that came from Humphreys with us are quarentined for measles for 14 days. Luck for me I didn't get locked up too.

Where is Mille now? What did she say about me for joining the army.

Must close now, hoping to hear from you by return mail so I will get it before I go across.

Your Brother,
Private Earl Young
401 Ponton Park
Camp Forest, Georgia

P.S. Tell Edw. he will like it after being in the army a while. I don't mind it much.

Well, dinner is over & was mighty well worth waiting for. Thot I would get my gun this morning but got put off till this afternoon. *The sun is out and has warmed up a little. You'll half to excuse this poor writing but I am using my mess kit for a writing desk to account for it.*

Did you ever hear how Mr. Harr's wheat & oats turned out? How are they all getting along? Does Paul still stop in there to fill his radiator. Ask him, but don't tell him I wanted to know. See.

What became of that saddle. What did you do with my clothes. Sell Paul that heavy overcoat of mine for 12 or 15 dollars. We don't ever get a pay day here or as yet we haven't. A few dollars might come handy in France.

Can you find out just what Herman Baumback's & Wesley Blackwell's address is. I would like awful well to ask them a few questions. There is a lot of the Eastern city, foreigners in the army, that can't talk or understand a civilized language. They can't behave any better than a lot of pigs at the table either.

Well a couple of the other fellows just came back from headquarters and say that we won't get our guns today.

Will roam around and see a few sights I guess.

As Ever,
Earl Young

11

Letters from Home

"Three Wonderful Letters from Home"
Song lyrics by Joe Goodwin and Ballard MacDonald,
music by James F. Hanley; 1918

Three letters left a village
Bound for somewhere over there,
Three letters to a lonesome soldier lad.
Each one a loving story told,
Each one was worth its weight in gold,
Three messages that made his poor heart glad.

For the first was just old fashioned,
And it breathed a mother's pray'r.
While the next one started, "Darling,
God protect you over there,"
And the third was filled with kisses,
Sent to Daddy across the foam,
From his mother, wife and baby,
Three wonderful letters from home.

Each word was like a soft caress,
That soothed his aching heart,

And drove away the misery and the pain.
Then joy returned to take their place
And brought a vision of each face,
As o'er and o'er he read their words again.

As Earl was getting acquainted with the boys at Camp Forrest, his sister, Millie, remained in Dalton with Laura. Millie knew Laura was very grateful for her help. There was no end of things to do and everything seemed to take twice as long when things didn't always go as planned. That was normally the case. There was not just laundry but fighting with the wringer on the washing machine. Not just cooking but watching the finicky cook stove so the roast didn't evaporate. And not just quilting but taking narrow stitches in poor lighting. The best times happened when the girls would just sit down for an afternoon cup of peppermint tea. Millie received her trunk with her winter clothes and was very grateful. There had been an early frost and some pretty cool nights and snow wasn't far off for western Nebraska. She also received a special treat from her mother: a beautiful, delicious, refreshing, unheard of commodity in Cheyenne County. Grapes—a welcome luxury.

Millie expected to find her princess slip pattern in the trunk but it wasn't there. She needed to write the folks and remind them to mail it to her. She was very anxious to make it, as she had found it in an issue of the French fashion journal *La Mode Illustree*. Pattern Number 0336. She had the material already. She paid the outrageous amount of 28 cents a yard to those crooks in Sidney. Now she was ready to sew, if only she had the pattern.

Nellie Young
Dalton Neb.
C/o Geo Young

Mrs. Joseph Young
Brock,
Nebraska.
Box 40.

Sept 10 1918

Dear folks!
            and hey
Rec'd your letter yesterday
and trunk today. The charges
were $3.85. Enough I say.
more than what the clothes
were worth you sent in it
I'm thinking. Why didn't
you send my ___ ___
pattern, I'm most sure its
in the envelope with its
picture on its out side in
the dresser drawer downstairs.
The grapes were fine. many
thanks!
      Laura and I bought us
some outing flannel

Mille Young
Dalton, Nebraska
Box 40
c/o Geo Young
Sept. 10, 1918

Dear folks,
 Rec'd your letter and key yesterday and trunk today. The charges were $3.85. Enough I say. More than what the clothes were worth you sent in it I'm thinking. Why didn't you send my princess slip pattern. I'm most sure it's in the envelope with its picture on its outside in the dresser drawer downstairs. The grapes were fine, many thanks.
 Laura and I bought us some outing flannel and was going to make us each a princess slip. Could wear it now these cool days. Had a heavy frost last Friday a.m. Some warmer today again, was going to rain but only sprinkled and went around us.
 Ed Dirk from Lone Wolf, Okla. and his father-in-law drove in Thursday. Ed is after a piece of this golden land out here. He and Osborne made out a contract today but he has until Wednesday to think it over. He has 580 A. in view with another agent and don't know yet which he wants. Geo. traded his piece for 320 A. joining his other quarter 13 miles west of here.
 Paul finished seeding his land Sunday and now he is barrowing George's again then he will be ready to sow too.
 I'm bunking with Miss Preston since Sept. 2ⁿᵈ, our school mam. Don't know how long she will get to stay. She is a nice girl my age, even shorter from Oakland, Nebraska. Got a card from Earl, he was on his way to a camp in Georgia but couldn't say what his address would be. He ask us to bake a cake and we made a raisin spice cake. Geo. and Paul butchered one of his old sows

last wk. so now we are having fresh meat every day. Fine weather for it so far, got it just in salt brine, never fried down any of it.

Well it's past bedtime already so must roll in cause 5 o'clock comes early now days.

Don't forget to send that pattern first chance you get or I'll have to get another.

Millie

Outing flannel out here is 28 cents and percale is 35 cents a yd.

The war raged in France. British and French troops needed relief that the U.S. could provide. They had been fighting the Kaiser for over three years now. This was the first time in American history that the United States sent soldiers abroad to defend foreign soil.

General John Joseph "Black Jack" Pershing was the commander of the American Expeditionary Forces. It was an incredible task to transport large numbers of American soldiers and equipment to the front.

Earl was doing his military training, taking care of one of Laura's W words—the war. He was one of the thousands of men who made the courageous decision to join the army. There was something deep inside him that made stopping the Kaiser more important to him than anything else. More important than the other Ws he could have just as easily gotten involved in. There was that one W—wheat. And the other W— women. But the W that loomed its massive presence over everything else had to come first—the war. Earl wasn't someone who could live his life as if the war and the Kaiser didn't exist. He looked forward to going overseas. He hoped he would come back. If he didn't, he was prepared to say it was worth the fight.

Earl's life revolved around reveille and retreat and all the things in between that made up the W of war.

OUR FIGHTING YANKEE BOY

Words and Music
by
John L. Galloway

PUB. by GALLOWAY MUSIC PUB. Co.
DETROIT, MICH. U.S.A.

12

Yankee Boy

"Our Fighting Yankee Boy"
A song by John L. Galloway, 1919

Preparing war for forty years
To crush democracy,
Was the plan of Germany,
To rule the land and sea,
But Britain, France, and Italy,
Just held the foe in check,
Till our Uncle Sammy joined his "Pals,"
And finished up the wreck.

When Sammy's work was finished
"Over There" in sunny France,
He turned his face to his dear old—U.S.A.,
The fighter with a will,
Who has caused the world to thrill;
For we are all aware,
Of the things he did to "Bill."

He promised Uncle Sammy,
When he sailed away to fight,
To make the tyrants pay the costs,
He did it too, all right.
A hundred million hearts are filled

With loving pride and joy:
All because of our own hero lad,
Our fighting Yankee Boy.

The battles of the Marne will always live in history:
As the blood bought liberty.
Of nations of the Free.
So since the work of our defenders "Over There" is thru,
Let us hope for peace forever,
With our old "Red, White and Blue."

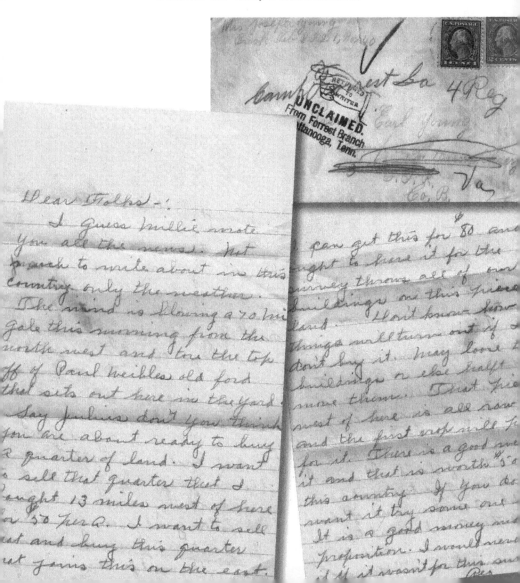

To: Mrs. Joseph Young
Brock, Nebr.
R.F.D. 1, Box 40
September 11, 1918

Dear Folks,

I guess Millie wrote you all the news. Not much to write about in this country, only the weather. The wind is blowing a 70 mi. gale this morning from the northwest and tore the top off of Paul Weibles old Ford that sits out here in the yard.

Say Julius don't you think you are about ready to buy a quarter of land. I want to sell that quarter that I bought 13 miles west of here for $50 per A. I want to sell that and buy this quarter that joins this on the east.

I can get this for $80 and ought to have it for the survey throws all of our buildings on this piece of land. Don't know how things will turn out if I don't buy it. May loose the buildings or else halft to move them. That piece west of here is all raw land and the first crop will pay for it. There is a good well on it and that is worth $500 in this country. If you don't want it try someone else. It is a good money making proposition. I would never sell it if it wasn't for this survey.

Let me know soon.

Geo.

Earl's suitcase collection

George and Julius were as hard working as their brother, Earl, taking care of the other W—wheat. Julius wasn't as anxious as Earl to join the army even though he loved his country. It was just that now wasn't a good time. Farming was how he defended his family and he was working every day to get enough money to buy a farm. George had offered him some land in western Nebraska. It seemed like a good investment: $50 an acre for some pretty good soil. Good enough to grow wheat anyway. If he got drafted, of course he would help fight. Maybe they didn't need him though. He'd just take care of himself and what was best for him and his family. He'd wait to join the army until it was necessary.

George definitely wasn't ready to follow General Pershing into France. He was working from dawn to sundown every day. All year. He reasoned that his contribution to the war effort was to grow wheat. The wheat would be turned into food to feed the soldiers. There were two fields of honor: the battlefields and the wheat fields. It took a lot of work to grow wheat. It was satisfying and he enjoyed it. Most of the time. But it was a struggle. There was never enough money. And when things seemed to be going good, something always seemed to happen. The tractor would break down, causing an unexpected major repair expense. You could work for eight months getting a wheat crop ready to harvest and a hailstorm would take it away in 15 minutes. How could he take time off to fight in a war? How could he leave Laura when they had just had their first baby girl? If he got drafted, he would go. But until then, George's world was consumed by two Ws—wheat and women, and he couldn't even think about anything else.

Villeneuve's collection in <u>One Hundred War Cartoons</u>; *George Colburn, cartoonist. Cartoons were also printed in the "Idaho Daily Statesman," starting in 1914, and continuing during WWI.*

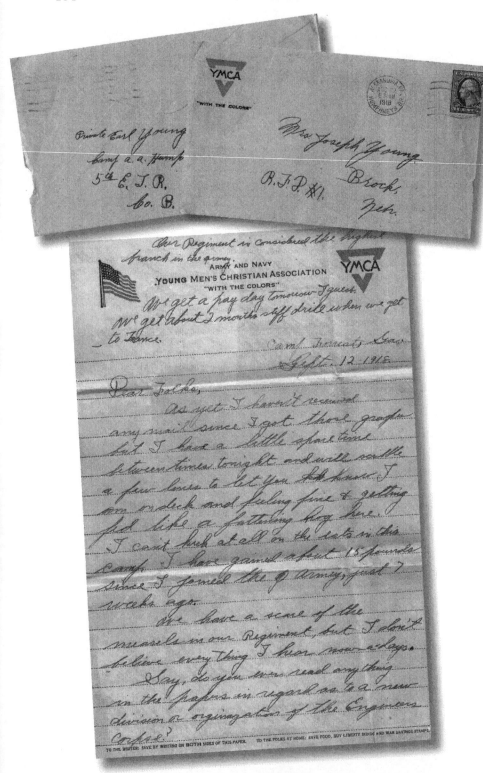

Private Earl Young
Camp A.A. Humphreys
5th E.T.R.
Co. B
Camp Forrest, Ga
Sept. 12, 1918

Dear Folks,

As yet I haven't received any mail since I got those grapes but I have a little spare time between times tonight and will scribble a few lines to let you know I am on deck and feeling fine & getting fed like a fattening hog here. I can't kick at all on the eats in this camp. I have gained about 15 pounds since I joined the army, just 7 weeks ago.

We have a scare of the measles in our Regiment, but I don't believe everything I hear now a days.

Say, do you ever read anything in the papers in regard as to a new division or organization of the Engineers Corpse?

If you do, you can bet your old hat that I am one of it. Our Regiment is the first one of its kind in existence in any army. Our Identification number is 207-E. We are billed for "over seas" and I find we have been since the 16ᵗʰ of last month.

Tuesday morning we leave this camp for an embarkment camp 18 miles from New York City, where we stay 8 or 10 days to get our "over seas" clothes & one thing or another before sailing.

All this sounds good to me for I am real anxious to get to France, have it over with and get back.

Our work will be to supply a Ponton bridge Regiment.

We have about 300 mules, 46 wagons, 15 saddles, and 16 trucks. They say we get "sawed off" shot guns when we get across.

I was just thinking today what a nice job Julius will have when he is drafted, if he does. We need a lot more stenographers, they call for them all the time. The typewriters click all night long in the Orderly Office.

Say, I don't remember whether I told you or not but when I was on my way out west last spring a insurance agent jumped me to take out a policy in the International life of St. Louis. Charlie & Mabel took out one, so I thot it would be real smart to have one too I guess so they signed me up for $2000 costing $57 per year. After I got out there I thot I was foolish I guess, for what I did so just never paid up and just let it go. The other day I got a notice to pay a note that the agent states that I signed. I don't really believe I signed my name, that he wrote it himself, & any way I am a minor & is illegal. I don't have the money to pay it now so will let you see to it that it is settled up just as you see fit with the least trouble. I guess the policy is a good one so maybe you had better pay it for me and then I will see if I can manage to save a little each month to met it.

I left the policy in my over coat pocket at Fred J. Harr, Dalton. Geo. never said whether he got my clothes from there or not, but if he didn't you can trust Mr. Harr has taken good care of my things for me. Trusting you will see about this at once. I will have a great load off my mind.

Did the government ever send you that policy of $10,000. If not it will reach you in turn, there is a lot of them to look after so don't worry if it don't reach you right away. It is in legal working order since the 27ᵗʰ of July all ready. Concert is just starting so must close. Girls from Chattanooga, Tenn.

Earl

P.S. I heard that Miss Hardin sent you some yarn for a sweater for me. I think she is very kind, because a sweater will come in as a real friend this winter.

The officers were saying this morning that we were to supply 5 other regiments with things and that we undoubtedly would be on the go all the time. That sounds good to me. Sure will get to see lots of country. We were out on a hike yesterday a.m. We went out through the wilderness about 3 miles & back carrying a 60 lb. pack and stepping 130 steps per minute. Somewhat like work, believe me.

Some of the fellows live around here that fought Sept 20, 1863 on this very ground. I was talking with one old confederate and he certainly can tell some wonderful stories.

I don't know any more to write so will close, hoping you all are as well & as happy as myself and that I get lots of letters from home when I get to France.

Write often to your son,
Private Earl
401 Ponton Park Engineers
Camp Forrest, Ga.

P.S. There is 2 boys from Iowa, 2 from Virginia & one from Michigan in this tent with me. They are all nice clean boys too. I have met 10 different Young's since in the army.

One fellow just came in and says the Captain went double time to the depot. All the other officers are all excited too. Maybe we'll move yet today. Can't tell. I think we go to New York City when we move. Send telegram if anything important to say. Will stay there 8 or 10 days. Will write more this evening.

Good By.
Will write from New York. Where is Millie.

Did you get those pictures? Will send some more soon. Can't take the Kodak across with me.

It is just 7:40 p.m. now and is raining the least bit outdoors. The soil is real sandy and of poor quality here.

I sure am glad I went to College last winter.

Must report to Company street.

Will write more soon.
Good Bye.

"A Soldier's Rosary"
Song lyrics by J. E. Dempsey, music by Joseph A. Burke; 1918

A mother's last words to ev'ry soldier,
"Kneel down at night and say your prayers."
But he's so weary, thro' days so dreary,
After all his trials and cares.
Don't worry mother, he serves his Maker,
When he serves his country's needs.
No matter where each act is a pray'r and
They form the links upon a soldier's beads.

For his thoughts keep turning homeward,
And their pray'rs come drifting back.
That's his chaplet and his guide to victory.
But bullets are his beads and on his knees he pleads,
That each one will help to end the misery.
Ev'ry shot a pearl, each pearl a pray'r,
He fights until he falls, "Lost in action" comes
The message o'er the sea.
And while the nation mourns his loss,
His dear old mother bears the cross.
That's a soldier's rosary.

When bells are tolling, our hearts consoling,
We seek the chapel o'er the way.
When cannons thunder, would we I wonder,
Ever take the time to pray.
The foe before him, no shelter o'er him,
Overhead the cold stars shine.
His Maker knows as onward he goes,
That his pray'r is better far than yours or mine.

"I for sure don't understand the logic of the army officers at Camp Forrest," Morgan said to Earl, genuinely perplexed.

"It is mighty hard to figure out. But let's get going before they change their minds about giving us an afternoon off," Earl said.

"Why did they decide to give us this time off now? We've been training hard night and day. When it's raining cats and dogs they order us on an extra-long march. Today the sun's out and they tell us we've got until 1900 hours to do what we want," Morgan said, still perplexed.

"My guess is that we will ship out over the pond very soon. And you can bet we won't get any time off when we're on the other side. This is probably our last hurrah for a while," Earl replied.

"So what are you going to do—write another letter I suppose?"

"I thought we'd do something different," Earl said.

"Like what? We don't have any money."

"Fishing."

"Great idea. Count me in," Morgan said. "Where do we go?"

"We know where the Chickamauga River is. Let's go there."

"I'm with you plowboy. Let's go," Morgan said.

The Georgia landscape was beautiful. Earl learned by studying his map that Georgia was the largest state east of the Mississippi. Both Morgan and Earl thought it was more scenic when the sun was shining than when it was pouring rain. The trees in the woods were thick, tall, and huge. Some of the large ones topped out at over 100 feet.

"The enormous size of these trees amazes me," Earl said. "The ones in Nebraska aren't nearly this big. It's interesting that the first American Arbor Day originated in Nebraska—a state that in some counties has no trees at all. You know, arbor means tree in Latin," Earl said then chuckled.

"Earl—I know you're proud of Nebraska but I think you are really stretching it. There are about the same number of trees in Nebraska as there are honest bankers in the United States. You're just making that story up about Arbor Day being founded in Nebraska. Aren't you?" asked Morgan.

"Honest and true. Arbor Day started in Nebraska City, just a few miles from my hometown of Brock. Arbor Day originated in Nebraska and that's why it's known as the Arbor State," Earl said proudly.

"They planted a million trees in Nebraska in the year they started Arbor Day," Earl continued.

"I think you might be confusing trees with tumbleweeds," Morgan teased. "Now let's talk about how we're going to catch some fish."

"Glad I brought you along on this fishing trip, Morgan," Earl said.

"Is that because I know where to dig for worms?"

"That's exactly why," Earl agreed.

"Now, if the trout would just cooperate," Morgan said.

"You boys can stay there for hours and you ain't going to catch as much as a pollywog," said the voice of an old man, who appeared from behind a large blackberry bush.

"Hi there, mister. Is this your property? Hope you don't mind us being here?" Earl said.

"No, I don't mind. But you're not fishing in the best spot. I'd be happy to show you where I throw my line in," the man said.

"We'd be much obliged," said Morgan. He held out his hand. "I'm Morgan and this is Earl."

The men exchanged handshakes. Earl noticed the roughness in the man's skin.

"My name's Benjamin Haines. But most people call me Reb," the man said as he ran one hand through his full, thick gray hair, scratching his full gray beard with the other hand.

"Follow me. I go rather slow on account of this cane, but it's just a short walk to where that outcropping of rocks are," Reb said. He pointed upstream about 200 yards.

"From the looks of you two, I imagine you're from one of the army bases around these parts. It doesn't really matter to me but are you two absent without leave?"

Earl and Morgan both laughed and said at the same time, "Got an afternoon off."

"Isn't that something? An afternoon off. What kind of army is that?" Reb said, like he hadn't heard of such a thing in his entire life. Things didn't work like that when he was in the military.

"An army that neither one of us can figure out," Morgan said.

"But you have to realize that we're just privates," Earl added.

"I was in the military. Had rank of first lieutenant," Reb said proudly. "I can tell by the way you boys talk that you're not from around here. What part of the country you boys from?" Reb asked.

"Michigan."

"Nebraska."

"I should have known. Both Yankees. I may regret showing you two my favorite fishing spot," Reb said. His voice was gruff. But he was smiling and had a twinkle in his eye, which relieved them both.

"You boys headed off to fight Germany?" Reb asked.

"Soon we'll be headed to France," Earl said.

"At least that's what they tell us," Morgan added.

"I fought in a war. In fact, Nebraska and Michigan were two of the states I was fightin' against," Reb said. His tone was very matter of fact. Earl and Morgan looked at each other, perplexed. Reb seemed to read their minds and said, "That's right boys. I was a first lieutenant for the Confederacy, under General Nathan Forrest's command."

Their jaws dropped and hung open as their minds were racing. Finally, Morgan asked, "You were in the Civil War?"

"I was a cavalry officer and proud to have fought to defend my state of Georgia for the Confederate States of America," Reb said.

Earl and Morgan were speechless. They didn't quite know what to say or how to say it. They were unsure how Lieutenant Benjamin Haines, or Reb that is, would react to whatever came out of their mouths. They were in the South after all. And Yankees. And they were sitting next to someone who had fought against the Yankees. Earl and Morgan relied on their vast two months of enlisted army service to respond. They shut up. Didn't utter a word. They seemed to be barely breathing. Reb took off his cap, light gray with large engraved letters that said CSA enclosed in a circle. He ran his fingers through his unruly gray hair then stroked his beard.

"I can tell that I've surprised you boys some," Reb drawled. "Don't you worry. I was proud to have fought for the Confederacy, but I'm equally proud to be an American. And I am proud of you boys for taking the fight to the Germans. That makes us comrades. I can appreciate your service and support whatever you can do to keep those Huns out of my beloved Georgia."

"Thank you for those kind words, Reb," Earl said.

"Yes, thank you for that," Morgan said, "I can tell you were as dedicated to your cause as we are to ours."

Reb nodded his head and rubbed his leg. "Got wounded in the Battle of Chattanooga in '63. My leg got infected and almost lost it. In fact, the sawbones in the camp wanted to take it off but I wouldn't let 'em. By the time I had recovered, the war was over. By the way boys, both of you have had a fish on the end of your lines for the last ten minutes," Reb said with a laugh. "Some fishermen you are!"

"To heck with the fish," Earl said. "We were just trying to get away from the army for a while. We'd much rather talk to you about the Civil War. We don't care about the fish."

"That's for sure," Morgan added.

"I'll tell you what boys. You bring those fish in. I'll take them and, in exchange, I'll tell you some history about this river and these woods," Reb said.

"That would be fine with us," Earl said, as Morgan nodded his head in agreement.

"I like you boys, even if you are Yankees," Reb said. "And I'm glad you're interested in hearing about the Civil War. Most of my family and the people around here don't want to hear anything about it. To them I am just an old relic—an old relic and rebel from the Confederacy. That's why they call me Reb."

"We'll try to keep track of any more fish on our lines," Earl said.

"We'll gladly listen to what you have to say," Morgan said.

"I'll tell you some things you probably don't know. There were a lot of battles in Georgia during the war. One of the fiercest battles of the entire war between the States was fought on this very ground. Camp Forrest, a few miles from this creek, was named to honor General Nathan B. Forrest," Reb said.

"Wow! So that's how Camp Forrest got its name," Morgan said.

"That's right. General Nathan Bedford Forrest was a hero in the Battle of Chickamauga. The battlefield later became Ft. Oglethorpe, which is now Camp Forrest. The army base sits right on the actual battlefield. It was fought fifty-five years ago this month. On September 19, 1863. How old are you boys?" Reb asked.

"Eighteen," they said at the same time.

"In September of 1863 I had just turned eighteen," Reb said, "I was the same age as you are now when I fought in the Civil War. So, as you can imagine, there aren't too many of us around that can say they fought at the Battle of Chattanooga."

"That's incredible," Morgan said. "I never thought I'd talk to a soldier from the Civil War."

"Wow. Same age, different wars," Earl said.

"And this river you're fishing in is the Chickamauga. It ran red with blood that day in September. Blood from both Union and Confederate soldiers."

"Oh Lord! That gives me the chills!" Earl shouted.

Morgan looked out at the river and imagined how it must have looked.

Reb stared at the river, his muscles tensing, his eyes not blinking, his mind lost in time. He cleared his throat, swallowed hard, then continued: "The fighting was ferocious at the Battle of Chattanooga. It was close-quartered and hand-to-hand. It turned out to be the bloodiest two-day battle of the entire Civil War. The dead were stacked just like cordwood after the battle. But the worst part was the wounded. Men from both armies lay between the lines. Cries and groans from those poor fellows were horrible. I'll never forget those sounds."

Earl and Morgan both swallowed hard. Twice. They were silent so Reb could continue his recollections without being pressed to do so.

Reb's voice stranded with emotion, his eyes filled with tears that cascaded down his face, and yet he still did not blink. "The storm of lead and cannonballs showered us from all sides. Billys and Johnnys lay side-by-side, unconscious or wounded. My horse, a black geld-

ing called Dark Knight, charged on the right flank of some
Union division. He and most of the thirty-two other horses in
my division got shot from under us. Just like a scythe mowing
down hay. Everything went black; I could hear but couldn't see.
About ten minutes later, my vision was returning. My eyes were
blurry from the smoke in the air, as thick as fog. Dead and
dying men, blue and gray, lay all around. Dead or worse.
Wounded horses were scattered over the battlefield. Cannons
were firing not far away. The ground shook and shrapnel zinged
through the air. I looked for the flag bearer of my Fourth Georgia
Cavalry but didn't see any soldiers from my unit still
standing. I went towards a group of Confederates from the
Sixth Texas near a stand of tall oaks." Reb paused again.

He stared at the river with no movement. He seemed to
be frozen. Images of that day were replaying in his head. Earl
and Morgan were entranced by Reb's story. Picturing the
battle. Picturing the river that ran red. A chill ran up Earl's
back and he visibly shuddered. The movement brought Reb
out of his trance and he continued.

"The fighting was pretty much over for the day. I stayed
with the Sixth Texas. Both sides were preparing feverishly for
the next day's fighting, knowing it would be just as fierce. The
Confederates had not broken the Union line, so we would prepare
to try again the following day. It was hot and our throats were
parched. We had possession of the Chickamaugua River and had
water. The Union boys had to do without." Reb paused again,
rubbing his leg. Harder this time.

"As darkness started to fall, we were ordered to rest. But there
would be little rest as the cries and groans of the wounded
continued. Just in front of the woods, a Union officer lay seriously

wounded. His cries were so pitiful and ongoing that it even started getting to the Texans. We couldn't bear to listen anymore. Two of us risked our lives by making a dash straight to where he was lying. In an instant, we lifted him up and carried him back behind our lines. We stuffed some pieces of a horse blanket in his wounds to stop the bleeding. Then we carried him farther away from Union positions, deeper into the woods. It was a clear violation of orders but we managed to start a fire and lay the Union soldier next to it."

"You helped save the life of an enemy soldier?" asked Morgan incredulously.

"I did. I can't explain it. Fighting and killing the blue bellies during the day. Then bandaging this Union soldier from Pennsylvania during the night. War is unexplainable. Totally unexplainable. I only know that I did what I thought was honorable and right."

Reb paused then stood up and rubbed his leg again. He took his hat off and ran his hands through his hair.

"Well boys, now you've heard my story. It's time for me to gather up those fish the Chickamauga gave up and go milk my cows."

Reb took the fish the boys had tied together and started back through the woods, leaning on his cane with each step.

"Hey Reb!" hollered Earl.

Reb turned around to look at the boys as they stood at the river's edge. Earl and Morgan stood straight at attention. They gave Reb the grandest salute they had ever given anyone. Reb straightened and threw back his shoulders. With a subtle smile and twinkle in his eyes, he tipped his hat, then turned and walked into the woods.

We're Building a Bridge to Berlin

The Mastersingers' War Song

WORDS BY

C.K. Gordon

MUSIC BY

Bart. E. Grady

.50

Band Parts .25   Orchestra Parts .25

BOSTON
OLIVER DITSON COMPANY
CHAS. H. DITSON & Co. NEW YORK. LYON & HEALY. CHICAGO.

13

Building a Bridge

"We're Building a Bridge to Berlin"
Song lyrics by C. K. Gordon, music by Bart E. Grady; 1918

There's a land of strife and hatred over the Rhine,
That's where the Yanks will go,
To land the knockout blow.
For Democracy has bid them break the line,
To civilize the country of the foe.
Berlin's their destination at the other end.
It's the city that they're driving for;
Twenty million fighters Uncle Sam can send
Beneath the Stars and Stripes to end the war.
It's the flag the Hun can't beat,
It's the flag that won't retreat.

We're building a bridge to Berlin, to Berlin, to Berlin.
We're going to get the Kaiser and his Potsdam crew.
We're building a bridge to Berlin, to Berlin, to Berlin. There'll
Be Yankee Doodle doings when the boys come thro'.

We have met the Hun already in the fight,
And he begins to feel the force of Yankee steel.
We have driven him across the Marne in flight,
And soon beyond the Rhine we'll hear him squeal.
For with the Allied Armies fighting under Foch,
We are on the road to victory;
We will never stop until we beat the Boche,
And all the world is safe for liberty.
So the Yankee boys will fight,
Til the Kaiser cries "Goodnight!"

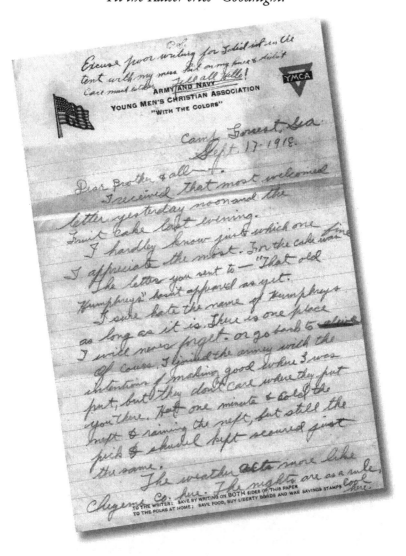

Camp Forrest, Ga
Sept. 17, 1918

Dear Brother & all,

I received that most welcomed letter yesterday noon and the Fruit cake last evening. I hardly know just which one I appreciate the most. For the cake was fine. The letter you sent to—"That old Humphreys" hasn't approved as yet.

I sure hate the name of Humphreys as long as it is. There is one place I will never forget. Or go back to ALIVE! Of course, I joined the army with the intentions of making good where I was put, but they don't care where they put you there. Hot one minute & cold the next & raining the next, but still the pick & Shovel kept scoured just the same. The weather acts more like Cheyenne Co. here. The nights are as a rule, cool here.

You ought to see some of the leftovers of the war of 1863 that sets around here on the old battlegrounds. (That battle took place Sept 20, 1863 on this ground.) There is some large monuments & steel tablets telling just which General fell & where & where he was from and everything. One low place—"a Lagoon like"—is called "the bloody pond". The steel tablet there says that that particular hole was one filled full of dead & dying men. OOOOOOO the shivers—

At Humphreys they had a dead show at the "Y" occasionally but here there is 4 or 5 large theaters that produce the real stuff. (The corn) See.

This camp is equipped to house 110,000 boys but hardly that number here now. I suppose Geo. has a saxon by this time? The Lieu. told us yesterday that we would get about 2 mo. training after getting to France, then forward to the front lines, then back to take up our work as Engineers.

*I find that there is only three divisions such as ours in the
army. One in France, one in the west & one here. Our regiment
consists of 2- 2ⁿᵈ Lieutenants, 1- 1ˢᵗ Lieu., our Captain, Seventeen
Sergeants & sixteen Corporals. No majors, generals and all of those
but simply direct under Pershing. See? The Regiment consists of
180 men and is called 401 Ponton Park Eng. Our serial number
is 207-E. We reported "ready" for "over sea" duty last Saturday by
telegram to D.C. and it only depends on time, that is anytime,
before we leave here. I look for it tomorrow or anyway this week.
I guess I will get to see Brod-way N. Y. before we go for a swim
across the blue frog Pond.*

Had a little drill this morning & a medical examination also.

*Just got a nice letter from sister Mabel this minute. Says she is
baking pumpkin pie and is sending something for the sweet tooth
she knows I have. slobber slobber slobber slobber Just wait till next
mail call. Mum. Mum.*

*I have about $1.50 left out of 35 I brought with me. No
pay day yet so there is lots coming soon. In France they keep of it
$15.00 that I can't draw. Maybe it's the best thing but I like to go
see the sights. See.*

*That Auburn paper sure was a treat. I didn't look at the chart
yet on it. Must close & answer Mabel's letter. Heard from Albin
Olson yesterday too. Do you ever see Paul Draper? Why don't
he write. Tell Edd. to write once too. Will send Kodak the last
minute. Maybe some exposed films for you to take care of. Ask
Ruth where to send them. Tell them Hello.*

*Private Earl Young
401 Ponton Park
Camp Forrest, Ga.*

Some mess. Liver, peas, spuds, lemonade til you have energy, white bread always.

Excuse poor writing for I did it in the tent with mess kit on my knees & don't care much either. Tell all Hello!

Earl enjoyed the fruitcake Millie and Laura had mailed. Even though it had quite a different taste than the other family fruitcakes he remembered. Maybe they used a different recipe. It was common during the war years to modify recipes to ration eggs, butter, milk, and wheat flour to help the Allies in Europe. Wheat flour and corn flour was not to be used because as much grain as possible was shipped overseas. The Royal Baking Powder Company even published a booklet entitled "Best War Time Recipes."

Eggless, Milkless, Butterless, Fruitcake

- 1 cup brown sugar
- 1 ½ cups water
- 1 cup seeded raisins
- 2 ounces citron, cut fine
- ½ cup shortening
- ½ teaspoon salt
- 1 teaspoon cinnamon
- 2 cups rye or barley flour
- 5 teaspoons baking powder

Boil sugar, water, fruit, shortening, salt, and spices together in saucepan for 3 minutes. When cool, add flour and baking powder which have been sifted together. Mix well. Bake in loaf pan in moderate oven for 45 minutes.

Laura was well known for the fruitcakes she made. She used a special recipe that had been handed down in her family for several generations. It was actually from a book that was published in the year 1833 called *The American Frugal Housewife*, written by Lydia Marie Child. Somehow, though, Laura's name appeared on the recipe card that she used to make the fruitcake for Earl.

Laura's Special Fruitcake

Four pounds of flour, three pounds of butter, three pounds of sugar, four pounds of currants, two pounds of raisins, twenty-four eggs, half a pint of brandy, or lemon-brandy, one ounce of mace, and three nutmegs. A little molasses makes it dark colored, which is desirable. Half a pound of citron improves it; but it is not necessary. To be baked two hours and a half or three hours.

Earl welcomed the fruitcakes, grapes, and other treats that were mailed to him by his family. It was their way of helping the war effort and ensuring that Earl would arrive in France in the best health possible. He would be shipping out soon. There were not many regiments like the 401st Engineers that Earl and Morgan were assigned to. The few army engineering regiments were desperately needed by British and French forces, and using army soldiers who specialized in this type of training was a new concept. At this stage of the war, the engineers were providing invaluable help. They could construct bridges, roads, and narrow-gauge railroads to both rear support and frontline action. They could use the forests to help build French ports or buildings. They could also use a rifle when necessary. It wasn't uncommon for these engineers to take heavy fire and have numerous casualties while they were doing their construction.

14

Billed for Overseas

Earl knew that he was going to have to hide from Morgan to ward off a checker-playing attempt if he had any hope of writing another letter to the folks at home. Earlier that day he had hooked a team of mules to a wagon to haul equipment for artillery training, and realized that a wagon might be a good place to write. Later, he climbed into a wagon parked under a large shade tree and used a smooth spot on the floor as his writing desk. Much better than using his canteen. And the daylight was better than the usual candlelight. As he was writing the letter, another soldier Earl knew stopped at the wagon. His name was Joseph Little.

"Hi Earl. Is a wagon really a good spot to write a letter?" asked Joseph.

"Hi Joseph. The wagon works just fine. I'd recommend it," Earl said.

"I actually just used a large rock to write on," Joseph said.

"I'm almost finished and will send it to my folks in Nebraska."

"I wrote a note on this postcard. Sending it to my brother in Chicago," Joseph said, as he held the postcard up for Earl to see. "I just need to find a stamp and I'll get this card in the post."

"I've got a stamp you can use if you show me your postcard," Earl replied.

"It's a great postcard. It has a lot of pictures of the area where we're doing our training," Joseph said as he showed the postcard to Earl.

GRAND REVIEW.

"OFFICERS FRONT AND CENTRE." U. S. CAVALRY.

ARTILLERY INSTRUCTION.

PHYSICAL DRILL, CAMP WARDEN MC LEAN.

Fort Oglethorpe and Chickamauga Park

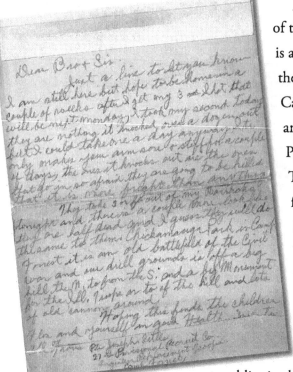

Joseph read the front of the postcard. "This is a souvenir folder of the Army Cantonment Camps, Fort Oglethorpe and Chickamauga Park, Chattanooga, Tennessee." He unfolded the card and handed it to Earl.

"Aren't these great drawings? I thought my brother would enjoy seeing what life is like for a soldier in the army," Joseph said, admiring the card once more.

Earl looked at the first drawing in the nine postcards that were hinged together. Each one was in color with great detail.

"North over field from Snodgrass Hill, showing Army Cantonment Camp," Earl said as he read the title of one of the drawings.

"That card depicts just what this army camp looks like," Joseph said.

Earl flipped the card over. "Battalion Drill, Camp Warden McLean. Look how the drawing shows the marching soldiers in a perfectly straight line. That's exactly how we're *supposed* to drill," Earl said and laughed.

Joseph laughed along with him.

"And when our lines aren't straight, we certainly hear about it," Earl said as he shook his head and plugged his ears at the thought.

It was hard enough marching at a pace of 130 steps a minute, but then the sergeants also demanded that the lines be perfectly straight when the privates marched. They were constantly corrected by sergeants about their formations. When they marched, their lines needed to be "straight as a ruler." It was apparently some sergeant's mission in life to drill privates on a daily basis until they performed flawlessly.

"Hm. The Post theatre and exchange. Camp Greenleaf. And Fort Oglethorpe," Earl noted as he kept flipping through the cards.

"Fort Oglethorpe is now the entrance to the Chickamauga National Military Park, the oldest and largest of the Civil War parks. The fort was built on the site of the Chickamauga battlefield. Amazingly, earlier today I actually talked with a Confederate soldier that told me about the history in this area," Earl added.

"That is incredible. I would imagine a Confederate soldier would have some interesting stories to tell," Joseph said.

"I'll tell you all about it later tonight. I just wrote some things I learned from him in the letter to my folks," Earl said, as he looked at the rest of the postcards. "The U.S. Cavalry—all mounted up and ready to go. Soldiers being instructed in artillery. Oh and can't leave out physical drill," Earl said as he admired the drawings.

"Don't remind me of physical drill. I thought the officer of the day would never have us stop doing push-ups this morning," Joseph complained.

"The drawings certainly show exactly what Camp Forrest looks like," Earl said.

"That's how the barracks look, that's how the trees look and the artist even shows exactly the color of the sky when the sun sets on the old camp at night," Joseph added.

"The last postcard on this side shows the U.S. Army Infantry band with men playing trombones, saxophones, and trumpets,"

Earl said, as he turned the folder over to see the drawings on the other side. "There are more Cantonment Camp pictures, the Army Y.M.C.A. Auditorium—"

"I really enjoy the shows at the Y, especially when the Red Cross nurses sing," Joseph interrupted.

"Just look at how well-made these beds are," Earl said then laughed as he looked at a drawing of the mess hall and sleeping quarters.

"That's right. Beds made according to army regulations, gear stored in our lockers exactly six inches, not five inches or seven inches. But six inches from the bed post and not a speck on the floor," Joseph emphasized.

"The last two cards are the grand review and gymnastic drill," Earl said, as he handed the postcard folder back to Joseph.

"Gymnastic drills! Now there's some exercises that will make you glad to fall into your bed at night. I'd rather hike twenty miles than do squats and somersaults for an hour," Joseph said then exhaled loudly and rubbed his legs. Just thinking about those squats made his legs ache.

"Here's the stamp for your postcard Joseph. Thanks for showing me those colorful postcards. Let's mail these letters and head to the mess hall."

Mr. W. J. Little
7723 Calumet Ave
Chicago, Ill

Dear Bro & Sis,

Just a line to let you know I am still here but hope to be home in a couple of weeks. After I get my 3rd shot, that will be next

Monday, I took my second today. They are nothing. It knocked over a dozen out but I could take one a day. Anyway, it only makes your arm sore & stiff for a couple of days. The ones it knocks out are the ones that go in so afraid they are going to be killed that it is more fright than anything.

They toke 3 or 4 out of my barracks tonight and there is a couple more looks like they are half dead I guess they will do the same to them. Chickamauga Park is Camp Forrest. It is an old battlefield of the Civil War and our drill grounds is off a big hill. The N. to from the S. and a big Monument for the Ill. Troops and to the hill and lots of old cannons around.

Hoping this finds the children, Flon and yourself in good health. Love to all of you.

Pvt Joseph Little
27ᵗʰ Provisional Recruit Co.
Engineer Replacement Troops
Camp Forrest
Lytle, Ga

Sometimes when Earl would mail a letter to one family member, it was placed in another envelope and forwarded to another family member.

Earl's September nineteenth letter from Camp Forrest was mailed to his brother George in Dalton, Nebraska. Laura, Mrs. George Young that is, then put the letter in a different envelope and forwarded the letter to Earl's sister, Millie, in Brock, Nebraska.

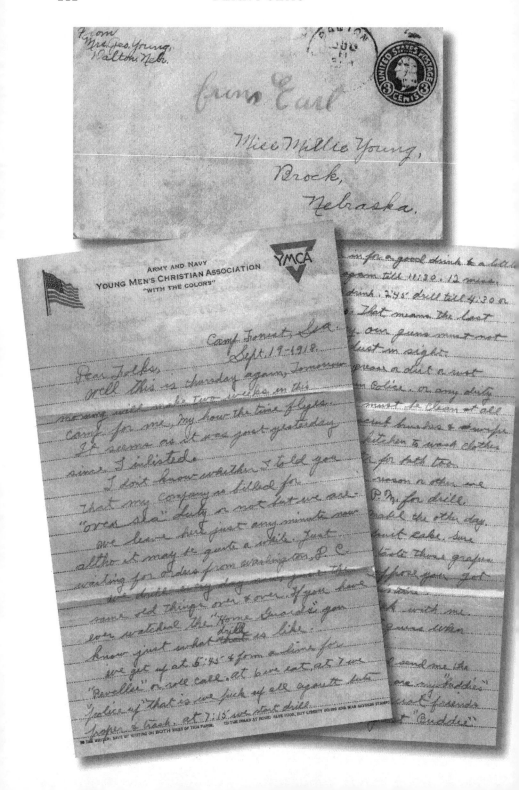

from Earl
Camp Forrest, Ga
Sept. 19, 1918

Dear Folks,

Well this is Thursday again. Tomorrow morning will make two weeks in this camp for me. My how the time flyes. It seems as it was just yesterday since I enlisted.

I don't know whether I told you that my company is billed for "over sea" duty or not but we are. We leave here just any minute now altho it may be quite a while. Just waiting for orders from Washington D.C.

We drill every day now, just the same old things over & over. If you have ever watched the "Home Guards" you know just what drill is like.

We get up at 5:45 & form a line for "Revellie" or roll call. At 6 we eat, at 7 we "police up" that is we pick up all cigarette butts, paper & trash. At 7:15 we start drill. At 9:30 we come in for a good drink & a little rest. 9:45 drill again till 11:30. 12 mess. 1 drill. 2:30 rest & drink. 2:45 drill till 4:30 or 5. Retreat at 5:30. That means the last formation of the day. Our guns must not have one speck of dust in sight. If there is any grease or dust or rust we get "K.P." or Kitchen Police, or any duty work. See. Clothes must be clean at all times. We use scrub brushes & swipe lye soap from the kitchen to wash clothes with. All cold water for bath too.

This noon, for some reason or other we won't go out till 2 p.m. for drill.

I heard from Geo. & Mabel the other day. Millie & Laura sent a fruit cake. Sure was a treat. I can still taste those grapes. They sure were fine. I suppose you got that pack of junk by this time.

I still have my Kodak with me. Will send it to Millie I
guess when the last minute comes. Were those pictures good.
Send me the best ones. The other fellows are my "buddies."
Everybody has several special friends in the army you know.
Just "Buddie"

The training Earl and the other doughboys were experiencing was serious, and created a lot of tension. Officers and sergeants wanted each doughboy to be the best they could be, trying to get the boys to do everything correctly and work rapidly. They wanted the pontoon bridges to be functional—not some of the time but all of the time. They wanted the boys to take care of the equipment so it would work when needed. Their lives and the lives of their buddies depended on how well they trained and how well they performed when they got to France.

The boys received their orders during an early morning reveille. Earl was pleased he was finally on his way to the last camp before they would cross the pond. They packed their gear that evening so they would be ready to travel to the last military post before sailing to France. Earl thought it grand that his buddie Morgan received the same orders and that they would be traveling together. Earl decided to write a postcard to his brother. This was a tenuous situation. The future was unknown. He wanted to let George know that his training was over and he would soon embark for France. It was time to say goodbye.

"We're Going Over"
A song by Andrew B. Sterling, Bernie Grossman,
and Arthur Lange; 1917

The major wrote the chorus but he fell down on the verse.
The colonel tried to write it, but he only made it worse.
They called in Captain Cuttle but it missed it by a mile,
So they left it to the Sergeant of the file.
Said he, 'We need no verse at all, to this here little thing,'
So they went and taught the Sammies how to sing.

We're going over, we're going over.
They want to settle up that fuss, and they put it up to us.
So what do we care, what do we care.
We'll go sailing across the foam;
And we'll show them what the Yankee doodle boys can do,
Then we'll all come marching home.

The boys all sang the chorus to the leader of the band.
He taught his men to play it, and it sounded mighty grand.
Said he, 'I'll write a part in for the fellow with the drum,
So the boys in France can hear us when we come.'
The orders came next morning, and they yelled we're on our way,
And they sang as they went sailing down the bay.

In Dalton, Nebraska, fall was in the air. The days were cooler and it rained more than usual. A few mornings had frost on the ground already. Farmers were trying to get multiple things accomplished. The rain wasn't helping. Of course farmers couldn't agree on the weather: Farmers who were seeding the winter wheat liked the moisture—it would help the wheat start to grow. Farmers who were threshing their wheat did not like the rain—they couldn't thresh if the wheat stalks were wet. They would argue with each other whether they wanted rain or not, as if they could vote rain or no rain.

Earl's sister, Millie, was taking care of the things she needed to do. She worked on sewing a dress in the evenings and during the day, gathered the last remnants from the garden. This September day she gathered pumpkins and stored them in the cellar so they could use them throughout the winter. She dashed off a quick postcard to her mother.

Sept. 19, 1918

Dear Mother,

I say this country certainly agrees with me but you overestimate my size by sending your patterns. Size 42 waist and I am only a size 36. I only weigh 100 ½ lbs. now but feel fine. Look again in my patterns and see if mine isn't there. Can't very well use yours. We are sewing these fine days. Laura is making Donald a fine red wool batiste dress.

Rained all day Sunday and in the afternoon. Geo. is out there growing wheat yet. Will go to the horse races at Sidney Sat. if he gets done. Put 30 small squash pumpkins down cellar.

George got new Mitchell six & is still threshing.

Find patterns at once.

Millie

The boys received orders during an early morning reveille that it was time to leave. Earl was finally on his way to the last camp before they would cross the pond. He was pleased to be leaving Camp Humphreys on a ship that would take him by rivers to see more of the U.S.A. They packed their gear and boarded a ship. He thought it grand that his buddie Morgan was on board. Soon enough, Morgan was sleeping but Earl forced himself to stay awake through the night, studying his map so he knew exactly where they were.

The sun was just coming up over a harbor. Multi-colors from the sun reflected on the water. Earl heard a few soldiers coming up to the deck from somewhere below.

"Hey Earl, where the heck are we?" Morgan asked. He stretched his body and let out a deep yawn.

"My map tells me we've just come through Chesapeake Bay. That city over there is Baltimore," Earl said, pointing to a spot on the map.

"Baltimore? Where else have we been while I was sleeping?"

"We've been through Norfolk, Virginia, Washington D.C., a bunch of other cities along the coast. And now Baltimore," Earl said.

"Looks like we're pulling up to a pier," Morgan commented.

"Suppose there's any chance they'll let us off this crate for a while?"

"Chances are slim and none. I heard some of the officers say we were just stopping long enough to pick up some equipment to take to the next camp."

Earl looked at the water. "The big reason they don't want us to get off this ship is because of the influenza disease. A lot of the civilians have it and they don't want us army boys to get it," Earl said.

"Some of the army fellows had it at Camp Forrest," Morgan said. "It gave them the fits. I heard some kid from Indiana come down with it. He got a really high fever right away and perspired so much they filled a two-gallon bucket with his sweat. Three hours later they carried him off to the morgue."

The boys watched the activity on the pier—navy sailors helping load a number of boxes onto the ship, and children looking at the ships and loading going on. After a time, some of the girls started skipping rope. Soldiers on the ship's deck weren't that far away and could easily hear the rhymes they yelled out while skipping. They sang, one after another.

> *"Charlie Chaplin went to France*
> *To teach the ladies how to dance*
> *First the heel, then the toe,*
> *Then the splits and around you go!"*

> *"I had a little bird,*
> *Its name was Enza.*
> *I opened the window*
> *And in-flu-enza!"*

At first Earl thought it was funny. Then he said to Morgan, "You know, that's only funny if you don't have influenza." But Morgan still laughed at the end of that rhyme, every time.

There were a lot of rhymes, and Earl and Morgan listened and watched the girls as they sang.

> *"A sailor went to sea sea sea*
> *To see what he could see see see*
> *But all that he could see see see*
> *Was the bottom of the deep blue sea sea sea."*

> *"Postman, Postman do your duty*
> *Send this letter to an American beauty*
> *Don't you stop and don't delay*
> *Get it to her right away."*

As the ship got underway, Earl and Morgan walked over to the newly loaded supplies. They did a little rearranging and soon had two boxes of ammunition to sit on. Another box served as a table. As the ship sailed away from Baltimore and continued up the coast, the boys got out a trench checker set.

Earl was red. Morgan was black. Morgan was interested in the game as usual, but Earl was distracted by wanting to make notes on his map, to keep track of where he'd been so he could always tell his folks, and George and Laura, and all the others, the places he had seen.

"This is a great adventure for me, Morgan," Earl said and smiled broadly. "I've been in sixteen states in the last five months. Until recently, I'd never been out of the state of Nebraska. A lot of the fellows really can complain. But the army is giving me the opportunity to see things that I only knew existed on a map. To tell you the truth, I am having the time of my life! I don't even mind getting out of bed for roll call in the morning."

"Well, if you'd get your nose out of that map, I wouldn't have to do this," Morgan said, as he made a triple jump and removed three red checkers.

Sept. 20, 1918

Dear Brother,

It is raining this morning. Will move to embarkment camp I think before night. They took one blanket, 1 bed sack & barrack bag this morning so when you hear from me again I probably will be in New York.

Am sending my Kodak this morning. Ask Ruth about the films, some have been shot. (See). Several regiments leaving with us. Write to this address and things will follow immediately.

Private Earl Young
401 Ponton Park Engrs.
Camp Forrest, Ga.
Sept. 21

Good Bye.

Awful cool last night.
Sun shine in C. Fr.
All packed up now.

THE STATUE OF LIBERTY IS SMILING

WORDS BY
JACK MAHONEY

MUSIC BY
HALSEY K. MOHR

"The Statue of Liberty Is Smiling"
Song lyrics by Jack Mahoney, music by Halsey K. Mohr; 1918

Standing down the bay, in her grand array,
Liberty is watching there today.
For her heroes, khaki clad, and ev'ry sailor lad,
Their glorious, victorious returning makes her glad;
Her light is seen three thousand miles away,
The guardian angel of the U.S.A.

Now the Statue of Liberty is smiling,
As she gazes across the sea.
And the gleam in her glance
Lights the way back from France,
The beacon light of victory.
Her torch of freedom burning
Will brighten the miles.
To make their glad returning
A bright lane of smiles.
For the Statue of Liberty is smiling,
On the hearts of the world today.

Goddess of light, daughter of the Right,
Emblematic of the nation's might.
In her universal fame, we voice her noble fame,
So dutiful and beautiful, the glory of her flame;
Triumphantly her banner is unfurled,
The virgin benefactress of the world.

"Wow, Earl. Look at that! I've seen photographs of the Statue of Liberty in some of my schoolbooks. I always hoped to see it with my own eyes someday," said Morgan.

"Well, there it is, for sure. Just looking at that blue statue of a lady holding a candle over her head gives me a lump in my throat," Earl said, swallowing hard.

"Me too Earl," said Morgan. "But what are you—color-blind? The Statue of Liberty is green, not blue. And that's not a candle she's holding. It's a torch."

"Green? Doesn't look green to me. Maybe kind of a bluish green though," Earl said. "And how do you know that's a torch and not a candle?"

"That's because I wrote a report on the Statue of Liberty when I was in school. I had a book from the library that told me all about it," Morgan said. "Got a good score on that report too."

"I'm certainly glad I'm standing next to an expert," Earl said.

"That's right. As a self-proclaimed expert, I know the Statue of Liberty is made out of copper. And sitting in this harbor with all the salt air—that's what turns the copper that blue-green color," Morgan said. "Just go ahead and ask me anything you want to know."

"All right Mister Expert. What's that clipboard she's holding in her left hand?" asked Earl.

"That's not a clipboard! It's a tablet that's inscribed July 4, 1776. I'm sure you know that date in history. Any plowboy knows that, surely," Morgan said.

"Yep. That's when we declared our independence over the Brits," Earl said then continued, "I know Britain didn't send us that statue to congratulate us for beating them in the Revolutionary War."

"Right. The Statue of Liberty was a gift of friendship from France," Morgan said.

"I know France gave it to us but when did they do that?" Earl asked.

"I just happen to know the answer to that question too. It was in 1886. The reason they gave it to us was to honor the centennial of the U.S.A. And that's why Lady Liberty is holding a tablet. Not a clipboard. With the date 1776," Morgan explained.

"As I recall from my schoolbooks, France was on America's side during the Revolutionary War," Earl said.

"So you know some history too," Morgan said.

"I know France helped us both on land and sea. They provided us with military aid. And sent us men to fight for our independence against Great Britain." Earl continued, "I think it's interesting to read about the different countries in the world and the wars they fought against each other."

"It is interesting. I would say that when you're looking at the Statue of Liberty, you're looking at history," Morgan replied.

"History? Yeah, I guess so. And where we're headed we are going to add another chapter to that Lady Liberty on this September morn," Earl said.

"Well, think about this. During the French and Indian War, the Brits defeated the French and forced them out of North America. So a few years later, France wanted to even things up and helped the United States fight against Britain during the Revolutionary War. So now, here you and I and the other soldiers on this ship are headed to France to help them out," Morgan said.

Earl scratched his head and ran his hands through his hair. "And at this point in history, the U.S., Britain, and France are all on the same side. I think it's kind of confusing to learn who was on whose side and when they were on whose side," Earl said with a puzzled look.

"It's confusing just to hear you talk sometimes."

"No, listen. In just the last hundred years or so, during the French and Indian War, the colonists and Britain fought against France. Then a few years later, France and the United States teamed up to fight against Britain. And now the U.S. is getting involved in a war, with Britain on our side, to help France," Earl said.

"Guess we'll have to leave it up to Woodrow to figure this all out," Morgan said.

"As in President Woodrow Wilson?" Earl said.

"Yep. That's who decided we needed to get involved in this war. And that's why you and I are in the army, standing on this ship looking at the Statue of Liberty," Morgan said.

The ship slowed as it entered the harbor. The deck was filled with soldiers, most awestruck by the beauty. Those standing on deck were moved to remove their caps. Lady Liberty deserved their respect—a gesture each man obeyed without any order needed from a superior rank. It was a gesture that came from the heart.

"I remember in 1917, Woodrow Wilson's campaign slogan was: 'He kept us out of war,'" Morgan said as he rubbed his chin to help him remember the exact wording of the slogan.

"So much for campaign promises," Earl said as he shook his head. "But let's not talk politics."

"Ask me a question I might be able to answer. Ask me something else about the Statue while she is still in view. It's not often one would be standing right next to an expert on a subject while one is actually looking at the subject," Morgan said.

"Okay, Mister Expert. Just how tall is Miss Liberty?" Earl asked.

"Three hundred feet. Three hundred five to be exact."

"How'd you know that?"

"I told you. I got a good score on my report," Morgan said proudly. "Also her nose is four feet long, her mouth is three feet wide and her waist is thirty-five feet in diameter"

"Wow! The Statue of Liberty is certainly impressive. The size, the color, what it stands for." Earl paused. "It is one of the greatest things I have ever seen. And I am also impressed by all the facts you know about the statue, Morgan."

"Thanks Earl. Some people are experts on threshing wheat. Some are experts on the Statue of Liberty."

"I will have the image of the statue etched firmly in my head when I land in Germany or France. It will remind me of why I am fighting to rid the world of the Kaiser!" Earl said.

"If you end up in France, you may see something designed by the same guy that designed the Statue of Liberty," Morgan said.

"What's that?" Earl asked.

"It's the Eiffel tower. In Paris. Wouldn't that be something? Only we're not going to France to sightsee. We've got to stop that Kaiser from taking over France. Or there won't be any Eiffel tower for anyone to look at," Earl said and clenched his jaw tight.

Earl Young
401 Ponton Park Camp Forrest
Somewhere in U.S.A.
Sept. 24th, 1918

Dear Folks,

Such is life in the armey. I never realized so much before that a back-woods man from Brock, Nebr. could ever be permitted to get to see so much of the world and get by with it. It has only been since July 27th since I left Sidney and just think, I have went crosswise of nearly ½ the states in the Union and through some of them three times.

I hardly know just what to say next, so will just start in where I left off I guess.

We didn't get away from Camp Forrest, Ga till Sat. noon the 21ˢᵗ. Came north through Tennessee, Virginia, Maryland, Delaware, New Jersey & New York and am on Long Island, New York now.

I kept tab of some of the cities as we came through. They are Briscoe, Roanoke, Washington D.C., Baltimore, Wilmington, Philadelphia, Elizabeth, crossed Newark Bay into Jersey City. We then got on a big steamer about 4 p.m. yesterday & rode across New York harbor, crossed under several wonderfully large bridges, saw the Statue of Liberty or "Sept. morn" as some call it. Just a large blue monument of a lady holding a candle over her head.

Have seen several submarine chasers all ready but the submarine hasn't appeared yet.

We got here at midnight last night. We had those heavy packs and rifles to pack about a mile. When I got here I put my shelter half on my spring cot, with my rain coat and slept between one woolen blanket. Also had a midnight shower bath. Sure am feeling fine this morning.

We are under quarantine here on account of measles. Two or three have had a little touch of it in the last 2 weeks. "In my Regiment."

Oh! My! Talk about the Eats! All of the large towns along the road—the Red Cross—gave us apples, cookies, gum, cigarettes, sandwiches & coffee, galore!

Uncle Sam feeds just as tho we were kings, too, since we left Humphreys.

The morning papers just states that 5 died in this camp of neumonia yesterday.

The influenza is bothering a little too, but this is a large camp and such a little number, don't seem to amount to anything. (Bothers civilians mostly.)

Don't know of much to write this time so am finding it rather a hard task.

I sure wish I had a sweater.

We will be here just long enough to let the officers get things straightened out and get our woolen suits issued. That might be 24 hrs. & maybe 2 weeks.

Must close and clean my rifle up. A few rust spots have gathered while on the trip. Tell Dad I will know more about taking care of the old shot gun when I get back.

I don't really think the war can last very much longer, especially when I get there. Must close and get busy. Answer soon,

Your son,
Private Earl Young
401 Ponton Park Engineers
Upton, New York

Wed. Morning. They gave me No. 11E shoes, hob nails & steel toed. Weight about 110 lbs. Tell Mabel & Geo. I can't write anymore here. Send them this if you wish. Please keep track of all letters I send as I think they will be nice to look at when I get back.

"Well, here we are Earl. I talked with another soldier who's been here for almost a week. He said that our training is going to get a lot more realistic. We're gonna drill with gas masks. They'll teach us how to use them then they'll put us in these rooms and pump in poison gas. They'll know real quick who was paying attention about using a gas mask," Morgan said.

"Real poison gas? Just like on the battlefield?" Earl said.

"That's what he said. That way we'll have some experience. This is where they teach us about trench warfare and chemical weapons."

"Guess we have to learn about that. Just in case we have to do something other than build pontoon bridges," Earl replied. "I can hardly wait for reveille tomorrow," he said sarcastically.

"Reveille. Right. That reminds me of something else he told me," Morgan said.

"What."

"Have you heard that song that's really popular right now—called *Oh, How I Hate to Get Up in the Morning*?"

"I have. That's a great song," Earl said.

"Know who wrote it?"

"No. But I think you're getting ready to tell me."

"It was written by a soldier. A private just like us who is at Camp Upton," Morgan said. "A song writer who's a soldier. That's as bad as a plowboy who's a soldier. His name is Irving Berlin. We're gonna hear him sing at the vaudeville show tonight. The song's about reveille. He wrote it specifically for the reason that he hated to get up so early in the morning."

15

Standing By for Over There

"Oh! How I Hate to Get Up in the Morning"
A song by Irving Berlin, 1918

The other day I chanced to meet a soldier friend of mine;
He'd been in camp for sev'ral weeks and he was looking fine.
His muscles had developed and his cheeks were rosy red.
I asked him how he liked the life, and this is what he said:

"Oh! How I hate to get up in the morning.
Oh! How I'd love to remain in bed;
For the hardest blow of all is to hear the bugler call;
You've got to get up, you've got to get up;
You've got to get up this morning!

A bugler in the army is the luckiest of men;
He wakes the boys at five and then goes back to bed again.
He doesn't have to blow again until the afternoon.
If ev'rything goes well with me, I'll be a bugler soon.

Camp Upton, New York
Sept. 26, 1918

Dear Brother,

Gas! Gas! Gas! Is all I heard all day. We had gas mask drill today and must say it sure is interesting as well as pleasant work. We were at it all day—learning the different parts, how to take care of it, how to get it on and how to get the gas from the mask if any should happen to be there. I guess we will get to go through the gas chambers tomorrow if it isn't raining to much or if we don't leave here.

Tuesday & Wed. we spent just getting fitted out with heavy woolen clothes and hauling the old ones back to the warehouse. I & 6 other fellows got "special detail" work and had to handle all the clothes—going & coming. The moth balls were strong in the new ones but, well I don't know what was wrong with the old ones but they sure were sickening to handle—. Didn't have a gas mask yet.

I have felt better today than any time since I have enlisted. Time sure does fly. Two months today since I went to Sidney the last time and if it hadn't been for some of the fellows getting the measles I probably would be on the center of the Atlantic by this time.

We may be transferred to an embarkment camp any minute now. I thot that this Upton was such, but got entirely fooled. We privates never know when we will go nor where. All we do is stand by and be ready. Do what we are told, then if there is any kick coming we report to the officers. If treatment is unjust the fellow that gave orders had better look out.

If I get ahold of some DOE before I go across I will get some large pictures taken with my new uniform. Wrap leggings, woolen trousers, cotton fleece shirts and little jockey cap. No. 11E hob nailed steel toe shoes. They weigh about 6 lbs. per pair. See picture on this sheet. We each have 2 pairs. Nearly kills a fellow to pack them. Let alone a pack on back. Our pack weighs about 65 or 70 lbs. I guess and we don't have heavy socks, underwear, or helmet or gas mask or pick & shovel yet either, nor any ammunition in the gun, weighs about 11 lbs. extra. Now believe me I will need lots of practice to carry all this 30 miles a day & get by with it. It will weigh I expect 100 lbs. when fully equipped.

It is raining a little this evening. Must close but will need to bum some stamps to send this. Just got paid $2 since I enlisted.

Expecting to hear from you all very soon. I will close & go to bed. Hoping this finds you all well & prospering.

Private Earl Young
401 Ponton Park Engineers
Camp Upton, New York

P.S. The shoe is actual shoe size. Some shoe. Largest in company. They just came with the ambulance & got two of our men. I can't find what the disease is. Measels I guess.

A few scattering pictures. Would like to have one of each good one I sent you to get finished.

"That bayonet practice this morning was something else, wasn't it?" Morgan said. "Those officers barely let us catch our breath before they had us charging at those dummies again."

"I guess they want us prepared for anything. I thought by being in the engineering corps we'd just be doing construction work. Just think about all the other stuff they've had us doing this week," Earl said.

"Gas masks. Learning about chemical weapons."

"Infantry drill. Learning how to charge. And retreat."

"Shooting practice with our rifles."

"Explosives."

"Next thing you know they'll be having us drive a tank."

"Maybe. Who knows?" Morgan stated.

"Thankfully most of our time has been learning about bridge building," Earl said.

"Yeah. How soon do you think we'll board a ship to go to France?" asked Morgan.

"It could be ten minutes from now. It could be tomorrow. It could be in a week or two weeks."

"I know. The suspense is killing my appetite," Morgan complained.

"I don't know if it's the suspense that's killing your appetite —maybe it's that new habit you started."

"Oh, you mean my chewing tobacco?" Morgan reached in his back pocket, took out a wad, and stuck it in his mouth.

"You should try this brand, Earl. Maybe it won't burn your throat," Morgan kidded.

"How'd you get started using chewing tobacco?" Earl asked.

"It came in a package that was sent from a ladies aid society. They send things to soldiers in support of the war effort. This one's a Big Chief. It's got a bit of a tang to it. Care to have a pinch?" Morgan asked.

Earl grabbed a pinch and tucked it under his lip as he read a sobering newspaper article regarding soldiers from an army camp in Georgia who were lost at sea.

"Listen to this," Earl said, then read aloud from the paper.

The Atlanta Georgian

October 1918

On the morning of September 25, 1918, 690 infantrymen from Fort Screven, Georgia, boarded the old British liner Otranto and set sail for England. The Otranto was a passenger liner that had been pressed into military service by the British Royal Navy. While at sea the Otranto encountered a storm with gale-force winds. A tremendous wave forced another troopship to ram into the Otranto. The ships broke apart and quickly sank. Approximately 370 soldiers were killed.

"Don't think I'll be telling the folks about this story. It will just worry them," Earl said.

"Are you going to tell them what we learned about poison gas?" Morgan asked.

"I don't know, Morgan. What should I tell them?" Earl was perturbed at the question.

"That tear gas causes temporary blindness and serious injury to your lungs. That chlorine gas attacks your eyes and lungs. Phosgene gas causes a delayed effect on your lungs and then you cough until you die. Mustard gas causes severe damage to your lungs and death from asphyxiation, and—" Morgan said then took a deep breath. "Just talking about it makes me breathe differently. Our gas masks don't really work against mustard gas, Earl. You smelled the clothes. It goes right through and gives you blisters on your skin and inside you! If we're exposed too long to any of these gases, it could blind us or send us to a drawn out, agonizing death." He was suddenly depressed.

"Uh—I think I'll just tell them we carry our gas masks wherever we go and if we put them on, the gas won't bother us. That way they won't worry too much about me when we get sent to the front," Earl reasoned.

During a morning water break from gas mask practice, Earl continued his unfinished letter from the previous day.

Friday 11 a.m.

Well we were out to gas drill this morning. We had a few tests before going through the gas chamber. I got mine on in good time. Just as required. 5 out of five times and in 5 seconds. That includes holding breath, taking gas mask from satchel and putting it on.

We were in twice for two kinds of gas. First we went in and stood awhile. Then orders were "take off masks." This was tear gas and surely it has a good name. It burns the lungs a trifle but don't get worse. It makes the tears run in a stream and burns the eyes something fierce. It will make a fellow blind if one gets to much of it. The other, called <u>caloride</u> gas means death with just 6 or 8 breaths. 4 or 5 knocks one out so he don't know anything. <u>"If that is possible".</u> We always carry the masks with us "over there," so really there isn't much danger if we don't get excited.

Some of the fellows are "kiddin" me now. They say "tell her you won't get to see her anymore." Somebody is always talking. I have picked up a little myself I guess. They never get the best end anyway.

We are all waiting for another medical examination now. Shoes & socks off. Shirt & under shirt off. It is pretty cool this morning so I am just prepared for a seconds time to STIFF.

You will kindly excuse this poor scribbling, for I have nothing but a little book 3 by 6 in. sq. for a desk. This is the first camp that I haven't been able to get straightened up in.

Really I believe the sun has taken to rising in the South. The streets don't run straight with the world here anyway.

They give us cards to address to you when we go across. We leave the cards here in this country, then when the Govt. telegrams that we arrived there they are sent out. It reaches you two or three weeks earlier that way. See?

It might be quite a while before we go now. It might be 10 min. We usually move shortly after an examination tho. See?

So goodby, and write soon.
Earl

"Is it just me or do things feel different around here tonight?" Morgan asked.

"It's not you, Morgan," Earl agreed. "You can tell that something is definitely happening. And I'll give you three guesses what it is. One—"

"We're going to be playing checkers with General Pershing tonight," Morgan said.

"Good guess, but no. Two—"

"They're going to let us all go home tomorrow."

"No, I don't think so. One more guess."

"Tomorrow we get an all-expense paid trip to France."

"Bingo!"

Villeneuve's collection in <u>One Hundred War Cartoons</u>*; George Colburn, cartoonist. Cartoons were also printed in the "Idaho Daily Statesman," starting in 1914, and continuing during WWI.*

16

Crossing the Pond

"Set Aside Your Tears (Till the Boys Come Marching Home)"
A song by L. Wolfe Gilbert, Malvin Franklin,
and Anatol Friedland, 1917

Mothers, wives, and sweethearts true,
Hearken one and all.
Those you love have gone away,
To answer duty's call.
I see a teardrop in your eye,
You sadly weep and sigh.
As they are brave, let us be brave,
Make this our battle cry.

Set aside your tears for laughter,
Till the boys come marching home.
For we'll all be happy after
They return from 'cross the foam.
Let us pray for fair weather,
For the ones who dared to roam.
Set aside your tears for laughter,
Till the boys come marching home.

There are those who cannot go,
But still their hearts beat true.
What they do at home will show
Their loyalty to you.
For ev'ryone can help the cause,
There is so much to do.
If in your heart, you've done your part,
Then you're a hero, too.

Day One at Sea:

The boys were right. They just didn't know they were going to be right so early in the morning. Reveille was at 4:00 a.m. that day. Gear was packed. Prayers were said and they marched in formation onto the USS *Mongolia*—a 13,000-ton passenger ocean liner, originally built for the Pacific Mail Steamship Company. It was converted to a troopship that carried 4,800 soldiers.

Great billows of black smoke poured from the tall stacks of the ship. Earl watched in soberness as it smoothly pushed away from the pier. The smell of the ocean, the sound of seagulls squawking and flapping their wings—the clouds on the horizon forming a dazzling sunrise of orange and red, and the taste of sea salt in the air impacted all of Earl's senses at the same time. He thought of home in Nebraska and the different sights and sounds his folks were experiencing back on the farm: the smell of corn in the fields, the sound of farm animals as they awoke, the sight of sunlight sparkling on the early dew of buffalo grass, the taste of molasses in the air that wafted from the kitchen.

"You know what they say," Earl said, as he watched the spectacular sunrise.

"Yeah. Red sky in morning, sailors take warning. Red sky at night, sailors delight," Morgan responded.

"Let's just hope these sailors know what they're doing and we'll have a smooth sailing across the pond," Earl said in a hopeful voice.

"Wave goodbye to America," Morgan said.

And that's exactly what Earl did. He raised his arm and waved, and watched as the coast became smaller and smaller. Morgan didn't think Earl would actually take him literally about waving. But soon he also had an arm raised, waving goodbye.

"I have wanted to fight in this war. I am proud to be wearing this uniform. And I'm proud to be in the American Expeditionary Force," declared Earl. He gave one last wave of his arm. "We have trained hard, Morgan—and I feel like we're ready."

"I feel the same way," Morgan said. "I'm ready to be in France. To build bridges, dig trenches, or whatever I can do to help. If called on to fight, I'll fight long and hard."

It was only a short time since the ship had left, but all the boys could see was water in every direction.

"It's kind of creepy to only see ocean," Morgan said. His voice sounded a little hoarse. "How deep do you think it is right here?"

"I'm not sure. But I know a couple of things," Earl said.

"What's that?" Morgan's voice was even more hoarse.

"One, it's a good thing you didn't join the navy. All this water seems to make you a little nervous. And it doesn't matter how deep the water is. You'd never touch the bottom anyway," Earl said. His sarcasm wasn't helping.

"You're right. And you're not making me feel any better," Morgan said, as he looked away from the waves of the vast Atlantic to look at Earl. The look on Morgan's face was pleading with Earl to say anything to make him feel better.

"Something else I've noticed," Earl said.

"What's that?"

Earl smiled broadly. He wiggled his ears. A lot.

Morgan snorted then said, "I knew I could count on you to make me feel better!"

"This is just like being on the prairie in Nebraska," Earl said. "There are places you can stand on the prairie and all you can see is wheat—for miles and miles. Now all we can see for miles is ocean. Think of the waves like wheat blowing in the wind."

"They are going to get bigger and bigger," Morgan said. He shuddered. "Let's go see what they've got for chow on this tin bucket."

"You go ahead," said Earl. "I'm going to stand out here and look at it for a while. Soldiers talk about crossing the pond. This is the biggest pond I've ever seen. And now it's our turn." He was transfixed by the brightness of the water's glare and the smell of the salt water.

"Well, you can look at it as long as you want. But I can tell you one thing," Morgan said.

"What's that?"

"Your view isn't going to change for a week."

"I'm going to find out where the food is so I'm not last in line," Morgan said. "I heard some of the navy sailors on this ship say you take these stairs below deck. The galley is on the starboard side, whatever that means."

Earl stayed on deck for quite a while. He could see a rain-squall ahead, making the waves big. The wind was picking up, which apparently caused larger waves. In a few minutes, the rain chased him down to a lower level in the ship. After a number of wrong turns, he found Morgan sitting at a table drinking coffee.

"Finally found you, Morgan," Earl said and sat down across from him. "Why don't these sailors say left or right? Instead of port and starboard?"

"I don't know why they talk like that. It's a mystery. At least they don't talk gibberish in the army," Morgan said.

"Another funny thing they do? Just to keep us enlisted men confused . . ." Earl said.

"What's that?"

"Ranks in the navy are different than in the army. A captain in the navy is like a colonel in the army. But a captain in the army is like a lieutenant in the navy," Earl said.

"Thank God we're just privates, Earl. All we need to do is salute and take orders from anyone with bars on their collar."

Morgan took a sip of his hot coffee. "Gonna have some chow now, Earl?"

"Funny thing. Ever since I've come below deck I can feel the ship rolling even more. I have a feeling this plowboy is getting seasick," said Earl, then coughed.

"You're looking kind of green," Morgan said. "And it's a good thing you joined the army instead of the navy. You'd not only have to figure out where was port and where was starboard, you'd be sick all the time."

"We're on Our Way to France to Fight for Liberty"
Song lyrics by D. M. Buchanan, music by Ned Clay;
1917

America is now aroused,
The call from France we hear.
Ten million strong we're marching on,
We're coming with good cheer.

Your comrades France we're proud to be,
We'll fight for liberty.
And when it's over we'll leave your shore,
Your friends we'll always be.

We're on our way to help you,
We're sailing right along.
We're going to fight right by your side,
Until we right your wrong.
And when the fight is over,
Your friends we'll always be.
And we will teach our children's children
We fought for liberty.

We'll be in France, we'll have the chance,
To fight for liberty.
So now we're going after them,
In air, on land, and sea.
We have to fight for what is right,
To bring the perfect day.
And then, my friends, this earth will be
A happy place to stay.

Day Two at Sea:

"I'm not the only army soldier that looks green," Earl managed to say after looking at Morgan.

"And you're not the only one who is glad he didn't join the navy," Morgan replied, grabbing his stomach.

"Looks like you turned green just by keeping me company," Earl said as his stomach churned.

The quarters where the troops were stowed were rather unpleasant, so the boys went up on deck, hoping fresh air might help. Other country boys who had never been on the ocean were similarly afflicted. Watching other soldiers turn green didn't help. A couple of them seemed to be more than seasick, and those who had been the same green color the first day had turned a sickly pale blue. They were coughing relentlessly. Earl and Morgan were relieved to be topside to get away from the bad situation developing in the army section.

"I wonder why this ship has four smokestacks," Earl said.

"The simple answer is that the bigger the ship, the more smokestacks," Morgan said. "A lot of U.S. Navy transport ships are this size. The navy started with forty-five ships to cross the Atlantic. But now, there are only forty-three since the USS *President Lincoln* and the USS *Covington* sank earlier this year," Morgan said.

The day was overcast but it wasn't raining. Three whales surfaced close to a ship and their spouts sent a spray into the air. Earl poked Morgan to get his attention and pointed at the whales.

"That's a sight you don't see on the prairies in Nebraska,"Morgan said as he wiped his mouth.

"Let's hope we just see whales and no German U-boats.

There wasn't much conversation for the rest of the day. They were occupied with other physical considerations.

Day Three at Sea:

"When are we ever going to get our sea legs?" Earl said, lying in his bunk.

"Guess we have our sick legs, not our sea legs," Morgan moaned.

At times there was a slight easing of their vomiting and coughing. It was only temporary though as they would see soldiers in the bunks surrounding theirs, vomiting. Everyone seemed to be coughing, Earl and Morgan too, unable to stop themselves.

By that afternoon, they were doubled over, their bodies racked with misery. Earl struggled to sit up. He finally made it. He put his arms around his chest as he coughed, spitting up blood this time.

"Private Young, my name is Dr. Winston. How are you feeling?" the doctor asked.

Dr. Winston knew what Earl's, and Morgan's, condition was, good diagnostician that he was. Didn't take the dean of Harvard Medical School to know what was wrong. He only asked the question to easily determine how severe the boy's fatigue was. If Earl's response was weak, the doctor would add Earl's name to the influenza watch list.

"I'm really seasick, doc. It seems to be getting worse. I am just seasick, right?" Earl said and coughed violently. His ribs hurt bad. *Real bad.*

"Oh, you're seasick all right. You'll recover from that. But you and most of the other soldiers have bronchial pneumonia," the doctor said with a grim look. "Which is to say, you've all got the Spanish Influenza."

"I came here to fight the Huns . . . not fight influenza," Earl managed to say between coughs.

He held his chest again, in an effort to not cough. He tried to count to five in his head before he would allow himself to cough again. It didn't work and he coughed even louder. Dr. Winston walked two bunks away from Earl and took a soldier's hand to feel his pulse. He knew there would be none, and when confirmed he placed the soldier's hands across his chest: "Bloody Hell! This man is dead! Listen up, boys! This flu is dangerous. We have to do what we can to keep it contained. It's extremely contagious!"

Dr. Winston had been practicing medicine for 15 plus years. As an army surgeon, he'd seen everything. Or so he thought. This Spanish flu was deadly. Extremely. And like every other army doctor, he had few resources available to help prevent the spread of the disease.

"It got another of you boys," he said sadly.

He pulled a blanket over the soldier's face and was afraid to think about how many more soldiers he'd be covering. Dr. Winston lowered his head for a moment then walked back to Earl's bunk and sat down next to him. His body was heavy with exhaustion. He rested for a moment then took a deep breath. He slapped Earl on the knee to get his attention.

"Listen up, Private Young. The same goes for the lot of you boys. This Spanish flu is a killer. I've never seen anything like it. It spreads fast and can overwhelm your body's natural defenses. Your lungs fill with fluid, causing an uncontrollable hemorrhaging and you can suffocate to death."

Dr. Winston paused to let his words resonate.

"So listen. We don't have any medicine to give you. What you need to do is drink lots of fluids. I know you don't feel like it, but that's what you must do. And don't move around too much. Lie down and rest." *Oh God!*

Dr. Winston struggled to come up with anything more to treat the sick men. A few of the soldiers had symptoms when they boarded the ship. The speed that this influenza moved was unknown to medical science. This was only the third day at sea. The ship sailed with 12,392 men on board. As of now, 2,241 men had influenza. The flu had claimed the lives of five healthy, young army boys already. How many more would it claim before they reached France?

Day Four at Sea:

As impossible as it seemed to them, Earl and Morgan were not improved. In fact, they had become violently sick. Dizzy and struggling to breathe. A fever had them pouring out sweat. They coughed. They vomited. They coughed more.

"I don't think I'm going to make it," Morgan managed to say in a weakened voice.

"Don't talk like that, Morgan. We're going to make it," Earl said between coughs. "Just keep doing what the doctor said."

The coughing, the spitting up blood went on for hours. Their bodies, drenched in sweat. That afternoon, Morgan had an episode of coughing, so extremely violent and prolonged, he collapsed onto the floor, grasping his side. Earl, finding a reserve of strength somewhere and fearing for Morgan's life, knelt by his friend.

"Morgan! Morgan!" Earl shouted. Dr. Winston was soon kneeling by Morgan.

"Give me some room boys," Dr. Winston ordered. He felt Morgan's stomach and side.

"Bloody Hell! This man has coughed so hard he's tore all the muscles in his abdomen. Help me lift him up to his bunk."

Earl struggled not to cough. Then he coughed hard but somehow grabbed Morgan's feet. Several other soldiers helped by lifting Morgan's head and arms. Earl was amazed at how weak he was. Lifting two feet was too much for him. It took seven soldiers to lift Morgan from the floor onto his bunk.

The effort to move Morgan exhausted Earl's sick body. Dr. Winston encouraged him to lie down and rest, and sent a soldier to his medical supplies for wide bandages to wrap around Morgan's abdomen.

"Dr. Winston, a week ago I could carry a seventy-pound pack and march double-time for twelve miles. Now I can hardly lift a five-pound shoe off the floor!" Earl said dejectedly, all the time coughing to get through the sentence.

"The Spanish flu weakens you terribly," Dr. Winston said. "All that coughing and sweating takes the water out of your body. You need to keep replenishing it to get over the flu. You need to do it to survive."

"Sit up—eat some of this—soup, Morgan," Earl said in between coughs, while the doctor stood by to give the first bite.

"I can't," Morgan said.

"You've got to." Earl loudly slurped a spoonful of broth, hoping to whet Morgan's appetite.

With a great deal of effort, Morgan managed to sit up on his bunk. It took a couple minutes to get his bearings.

"Okay." Cough. "If you can do it so can I," he said.

Morgan let the doctor put a spoon full of broth to his mouth but started coughing before he could sip it. This scene was repeated over and over again the entire day.

Day Five at Sea:

Earl was determined to swallow a tablespoon of soup every 15 minutes. Since Morgan was too weak to even do this, Earl forced some soup into Morgan whenever he could.

"Here you go, Morgan," Earl said as he put a spoonful of soup to Morgan's mouth in between coughs.

"One for you." Cough. "And one for me." Cough.

All Morgan could do was lay on his bunk. Unable to sit up and too painful to move his arms, he needed help. His condition was serious. He managed to cough out a few words to Earl.

"I should've written to my folks," Morgan said. He coughed so hard the pain almost made him pass out.

"Yeah. Probably so, Morgan," Earl replied. Cough.

"If I don't make it, they'd at least have some letters I sent," Morgan said.

"You're going to make it. And so am I."

"How do you know?" asked Morgan.

"Cause we'd be lying on a cot with a blanket over our faces by now if it was going to get us," Earl said.

"You can't fool me plow—" Morgan's throat tightened up. He coughed then continued, "plowboy. You're thinking . . . this flu could do us in yet," Morgan said. He turned to the side to cough. Morgan saw blood spew out onto his bedding.

"One for you. One for me," Earl said and continued the soup, a tablespoon at a time, every few minutes. This went on the entire day. Coughing the entire time.

With eyes closed, Morgan held up his hand, signaling he was done and said: "Thanks for helping me, Earl." Morgan paused and showed a weak smile. "You'd make a good wife."

Earl looked at Morgan. They were both very sick. Earl attempted to wiggle his ears. Remarkably, he had so little strength, he couldn't even do that.

Day Six at Sea:

The coughing was endless and relentless. More soldiers had died. They lay on their bunks, their misery ended. A blanket pulled over their faces.

"Looks like you . . . made it through the . . . night, Morgan," Earl said.

"Thanks to . . . you." Both immediately knew from their first few words of the morning that their cough had not lessened.

"Not everyone did though."

"Who?"

"Lucas didn't make it. Also that boy from . . . Iowa," Earl said.

"The one that kept . . . trying to play the . . . harmonica?"

"Yeah."

"I could tell. He was turning blue yesterday."

"I liked him. Even though there were times I . . . really wanted to throw that harmonica of his under a—bridge."

"Yeah," Morgan said.

Later that day, after a particularly rough patch of coughing, Earl started bleeding through his nose. It would stop. Then it would start again. After a few hours, Morgan started bleeding through his ears. It would stop, then start again.

"Just because I've got a nose bleed . . . and a fever—do you have to copy everything I do?" Earl quizzed Morgan.

"It's not exactly copying. It's my ears. Not my nose," Morgan said.

"Oh, Okay." Earl tried to hold his head back. He pressed a handkerchief over his nose to attempt to stop it.

"Some soldier told me if I put a potato in my pocket that it would stop my nose bleed," Earl said.

"You try it?" Morgan asked.

"Couldn't find a potato," Earl said. "But I did find an onion. So I'm going to try tying it around my neck," Earl added. He dabbed the blood that was flowing from his nose again.

"Let me know if it helps," Morgan said.

The lights below deck dimmed. This was the signal for the weary soldiers to sleep. And pray. Pray that their health would return. Pray they would see France. Pray they had the chance to help end this horrible war. Pray that someday they could return to America. To see the Statue of Liberty again. To fish on the banks of the Missouri. To thresh wheat in Nebraska.

Earl closed his eyes to fall asleep, his breathing shallow and labored. He was uncertain if he would see the next day. But for now at least, this day was over. He had made it, and so had Morgan. As he fell asleep, an old hymn sang through his mind . . .

"Now the Day Is Over"
Hymn lyrics by Sabine Baring-Gould, 1865

Now the day is over,
Night is drawing nigh;
Shadows of the evening
Steal across the sky.

Jesus, grant the weary,
Calm and sweet repose;
With Thy tend'rest blessing
May our eyelids close.

Grant to little children
Visions bright of Thee;
Guard the sailors tossing
On the deep, blue sea.

When the morning wakens,
Then may I arise;
Pure, and fresh, and sinless
In Thy holy eyes.

Glory to the Father,
Glory to the Son;
And to Thee, blest Spirit,
Whilst all ages run.

Day Seven at Sea:

Earl and Morgan lay on their bunks all day. Time didn't matter. They slept, wiped their noses, and slurped soup when they could.

"Earl," said Morgan. "Did that onion work?"

"I think so. My nose bleed stopped."

"Mind if I borrow it?"

"Here." Earl untied the onion from around his neck and held it over the side of his top bunk for Morgan to grab it. "It makes your eyes water, I think, unless it's another symptom of the flu."

"Know what bothers me about getting this flu, Morgan?" Earl said.

"What?" said Morgan. He could barely reach the onion. When he touched it, it fell into his palm and he brought it in like a football.

"I'll be real upset if I die from the flu before we get to France."

"Cause you want to see how they farm in France?" Morgan said.

"I need to fight the Kaiser—we trained hard and were in good shape," Earl said.

"Yeah. I know."

Earl expected to be fighting the Huns, but never dreamed he'd be fighting for his life from the Spanish flu. Oh how that feeling would be stated over and over by many a soldier. Soldiers from Indiana, North Dakota, Idaho, and Kentucky had the same thoughts Earl did. He wanted to fight Germans instead of germs. He was so fatigued. Dejected. And sad. How could this happen to him? He had worked hard to be strong, to be able to fight. He had made the decision to become a soldier. He was proud, and now humbled that the flu had made him so weak. How long would it take him to regain his strength? Would he survive? Would he have a blanket pulled over his face too?

"Are we ever going to get there?" Morgan asked. He hadn't done anything with the onion yet.

"I'm beginning to wonder if the ship made a wrong turn somewhere," Earl said.

"Could be they went port when they should have went starboard," Morgan advised.

"I'll talk to the captain about that," Earl said.

"The captain in the army? Or the captain in the navy?" Morgan asked.

"Which ever one can put us on land. And soon. I've had enough of this," Earl said.

"Good luck with that, Earl." Morgan said. He finally gained enough energy to put the onion up to his throat. There was no brilliant sunrise of orange and red this day. It was gloomy, and the rain had yet to overcome the thick fog that surrounded the USS *Mongolia*.

Day Eight at Sea:

"You still alive, Earl?" asked Morgan.

"Guess so—still coughing."

"Privates," said Dr. Winston. "Welcome to France. You're so sick you probably didn't know we landed on the coast of France about an hour ago. At least you survived long enough to see it."

"Holy Cow! I thought once we landed, all this rocking and rolling in my head would go away," Earl said to the doctor.

"It doesn't go away right away. Give it a few days," Dr. Winston said.

"Remind me to never get on another ship again," Earl said, as he struggled to get his balance.

"My body doesn't believe we're not out on the ocean. This room is moving just like I'm on a merry-go-round," Morgan said.

17

Fight for Liberty

Sailors' Mail
Military Post Office

Mr. Geo. L. Young
Dalton, Nebraska

> ### THE SHIP ON WHICH I SAILED HAS ARRIVED
> ### SAFELY OVERSEAS.

Private Earl Young
401 Ponton Park Engineers

The postcard was correct. The ship crossed the Atlantic in good time, arriving on the coast of France in eight days. Earl was in critical condition with Spanish Influenza, so weak he could barely walk when the ship arrived in port. Many troops had contracted the flu, and the ones who survived it were too weakened and fatigued to fight and carry out their duties. WWI would claim 16 million lives while Spanish Influenza would claim 50 million. There would be 671 deaths on the troopship that took Earl to France, most of them related to the flu. Being in close quarters made it too easy to be exposed to the disease. They had crossed the pond but the fighting wouldn't be in bridge building or digging trenches or fighting the Hun.

It had been two weeks since they first arrived. Earl, Morgan, and many other soldiers were cared for in army hospitals throughout France. Coughing was subsiding. They were eating again and gaining weight.

Earl pushed up with his arms to get up from his chair. A few weeks ago he didn't have the strength to even accomplish that. He looked at Morgan as if he had just figured something out.

"I just realized I owe you many thanks for my recovery," Earl said with a big grin.

"You're thanking me for your recovery?" Morgan said, perplexed. "What are you talking about?"

"Big Chief."

"The chewing tobacco I gave you?" Morgan asked.

"Yeah. I chewed it just before we had shipped out. The way I figure it, that's what overpowered the flu germs. See? I owe it all to you. You and Big Chief."

Morgan looked at Earl, unsure whether he was joking or not.

"Huh. You're welcome, Earl. Glad to have helped, I guess."

Earl wiggled his ears. And then shook Morgan's hand.

"You are getting better. You can even wiggle your ears again," Morgan said excitedly.

Before the week was out, Earl and Morgan were hardly coughing. They underwent physical examinations, and the doctors pronounced them fit for duty. They were to report to their unit in the morning.

"So, we get to leave the hospital today and will sleep at the barracks to be ready to go in the morning," said Morgan. "I think we should play a few games of checkers tonight. It might be a long time before we have another chance."

"We better get to the chow hall and see if there's anything left. Then we can play some checkers," Earl said as he stood and stretched.

"What do you think dinner will be tonight, Morgan?"

"I don't know. But I can tell you this—it won't be sauerkraut," Morgan said, and slapped Earl on the back.

The boys settled in their bunks that night and the lights went out. Earl was thankful he was getting stronger. He was now close to being at full strength and looking forward to tomorrow. His unit would ride in boxcars for several miles and there, they would be assigned to light duty. As a soldier in the American Expeditionary Force, Earl was excited to finally be able to help participate in the liberation of France.

Injured soldiers had been admitted to the same hospital where soldiers were recovering from the flu. Earl was shocked to hear their stories. The devastation and suffering of the French people was astounding. The soldiers of the A.E.F. had been moved to compassion for them and produced many songs. When French entertainers came to the hospital to do shows, they danced and sang to them.

Falling asleep that night, Earl had one of those songs stuck in his head. It wasn't a restful sleep. He woke up intermittently, either coughing or because someone in another hospital bed was coughing. There was a lot of movement and tossing and turning. Whenever Earl woke up, the song was still replaying in his mind. He could hear a bell clanging. Was the clanging in his dreams as the song repeated in his mind? Was it outside the hospital? It was. A church bell from a nearby Catholic church was summoning the city to worship.

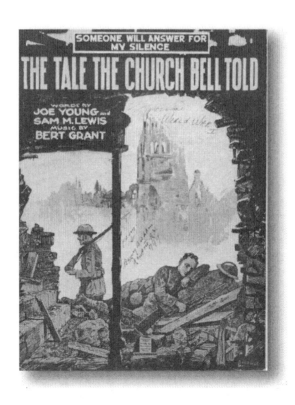

"The Tale the Church Bell Told"
Song lyrics by Sam M. Lewis and Joe Young,
music by Bert Grant; 1918

In the shattered part of France,
In the very heart of France,
A soldier from a Yankee shore
Lay dreaming by an old church door;
From the belfry in the sky,
He thought he heard the old bell sigh.

I was lonely in my steeple,
How I missed birds of spring;
Looking down upon my people,
It just broke my heart to ring;
Through the din of cannon thunder,
I could hear the cries of young and old;
Someone will answer for this vi'lence,
Answer for my silence,
That's the tale the church bell tolled.

Now the clouds have all rolled by,
Up here in a peaceful sky,
I'll ring again and then I'll see
My people coming back to me;
Ev'ry time they kneel to pray,
I'll dry their tears of yesterday.

18

The Frogs

"America Here's My Boy"
Song lyrics by Andrew B. Sterling, music by Arthur Lange; 1917

There's a million mothers knocking at the nation's door.
A million mothers, yes and they'll be millions more.
And while within each mother heart they pray,
Just hark what one brave mother has to say:

"America, I raised a boy for you.
America, you'll find him staunch and true.
Place a gun upon his shoulder, he is ready to die or do.
America, he is my only one, my hope, my pride and joy.
But if I had another, he would march beside his brother.
America, here's my boy."

There's a million mothers waiting by the fireside bright,
A million mothers, waiting for the call tonight.
And while within each heart there'll be a tear,
She'll watch her boy go marching with a cheer.

The reveille bugle woke Earl. For a moment he was unsure where he was, having been in the hospital for over two weeks. Slowly, reality hit. He exhaled several deep coughs. It was always worse in the morning, but he knew it would subside soon and started to prepare for duty. All his buddies were going through the same motions. Long johns on. Spats on. Wool coat buttoned. Metal hat in hand. Rifle clean and ready.

A booming voice called out, "Get a move on lads. Let's go! Let's go!" Although they were hurrying, they hurried even faster to get their boots laced. Out of the building they stormed.

Earl, Morgan, and the others who made up the unit of 183 troops fell into formation. It was raining as usual that month of October in France. A gentle mist was constant. The fog was thick. They lined up, four men deep. At attention. Ramrod straight. No movement. Earl struggled not to cough.

"Okay, men. After your name is called, grab a piece of equipment. Line up, so we can load it all up into the boxcars," ordered the officer in charge.

Earl readied himself to remain at attention until his name was called. With Young as a last name, he knew he'd be one of the last to leave formation—and so, his thoughts wandered as he stood at attention, waiting. *How soon would the war be over?* It had already been going on for several years, and now it was being fought in the mud, over some strange godforsaken land in France. But this is where the U.S. had decided to make its stand against Germany. They came into the war late, and with their allies, were attempting to stop the Kaiser from taking over. If France fell, then Germany would take over another country. It was time to stop them. To fight! To build pontoon bridges to bring in equipment to win a battle. To force Germany out of France.

Earl's mind drifted to his life growing up on a farm and was grateful for the ironic preparedness it had given him for this very moment in time. He thought about the reality that his relatives could be on German front lines. When his grandfather emigrated to America, he had left behind brothers and sisters. Some would be the same age as Earl. Were they German soldiers? Could they be on the front lines in France?

Grateful his recovering body was handling steady attention, Earl wondered what a light-duty day meant for the day's prep. He heard the immediate fight in the field would be mud and frogs. The mud always put up a huge fight. And today would be no different. A rainstorm in Nebraska most definitely brought out the frogs, but that didn't bother Earl. He recalled a conversation from a wounded sergeant at the hospital, talking about the onslaught of frogs in the trenches. It was miserable. Frogs were trapped in the trenches, constantly trying to climb out. Their failed attempts caused chaos as they'd splashed water and mud on the soldiers. Leaping. Leaping. Mud and water flying everywhere.

Earl thought of how much fun he'd had in Nebraska catching frogs. He ate them for dinner sometimes. But he'd never experienced them the way he'd heard tell. In France, there were thousands of them. In the trenches. In the rivers. In the way. Mud and frogs. What a war.

Earl held his breath. Swallowed slowly, doing everything he could not to cough while standing at attention. "Hagerman," the sergeant called. There was still a ways to go before he could move from his attention stance. His thoughts drifted again. He prayed.

He hoped the war would end soon. He was angry the flu had robbed him of strength. He thought about how German Shepherds at home were being shot, simply because of their breed name. He thought about the books that had been burned and destroyed because they were written in German. He thought about Nebraska, after the war, maybe he could help Julius and George grow wheat. He imagined playing with his new niece and how he'd like to scrape an apple into applesauce and feed it to her. He wondered if she looked like George or more like Laura.

"Keller. Kellington. King," the names continued.

Mist gathered and began dripping off Earl's helmet, and with the shift of wind, started dripping down his back. Earl thought about how wise his father was for changing the family name from Jung to Young. It seemed funny to him that if his last name had been left as Jung, he wouldn't still be standing in this formation at attention. *Earl Jung*, he thought. That sounds kind of strange. Earl's father, Joseph Jung, strongly believed the family's last name needed to be changed to reflect their new life in America. Earl remembered the day he felt brave enough to ask his father why.

They had been unhitching the horses at the end of the day when his father made a comment about the Fatherland. He told Earl that he had changed the name from Jung to Young before Earl was even born and explained the many opportunities in America compared to the old country. He described the ads he'd read, calling his heart to leave Germany. The journey from Germany had been rough. The women in the family had cried all the way across the ocean. When they finally arrived at the New York harbor, he changed his name. And from that time on, their descendants in America continued to be Youngs. The Youngs journeyed west—crossing 12 states to settle just west of the Missouri River, in Nebraska.

Earl remembered his father telling him that people do strange things because of a name. And he didn't want anyone judging him until they saw him for who he was: "I don't want someone forming an opinion about you just by seeing your last name, Earl, instead of first finding out what kind of person you really are. Prejudice in any form is wrong. There are those who see or hear the spelling of a last name and immediately form a negative opinion. People can be incredibly shallow when it comes to spelling. It's all in the spelling. Jung says German. Young says American."

"Young."

At the sound of his name, Earl was jolted back to the world in France. He was ordered to pick out a piece of equipment and carry it to load on the train. Earl's eyes shifted from one piece to the next. Naturally, what remained of the equipment to load was heavy: several boxes of ammunition, 60 pounds each. He picked up a 60-pound box, adding to the 70-pound pack already on his back, and started walking the 200 yards to the train. So much for light duty.

The train ride to the post was their first view of the French countryside. The fresh air was rejuvenating after spending weeks indoors. French rolling hills, tree orchards, farms. Earl contemplated how farms in France compared to farms in America.

The train had a number of boxcars. Some carried men. Others were loaded with equipment. It stopped about four miles away from camp, and the troops jumped out. They were ordered to organize the equipment. In the distance they could hear an occasional explosion. Earl noticed that each soldier had a firm grip on his rifle. Even though fighting at the front was not eminently near, one could not be too careful. A group of guys were huddled nearby, their helmets tilted upwards.

"There's a dogfight!" Earl overheard Patrick say.

Patrick was from a small town in Indiana. He seemed to be intently studying the sky. He played checkers with Earl and Morgan when one or the other was occupied writing letters home or standing guard or doing the dreaded KP.

Earl looked up. The sky was bright blue with fluffy white clouds like the ones that formed in western Nebraska summers. He watched as a plane dove towards the ground. Another followed closely behind. The first plane pulled up in a wide arc, and the one behind it followed the same arc and twisted and turned.

"They're fighting. Two of the planes are Brits. The other two are Krauts. I can tell by the markings on the planes," Patrick said.

The planes looped back and forth. They went through some turns in tighter circles, looking like wasps zooming around a nest.

"Fighting in the air! Now I've seen everything," Earl said. He would definitely have to write a letter tonight. The flu had made him so exhausted he had been too weak to write. He wanted to start a letter soon and this spurred him on.

The sound of gunfire from one of the planes snapped him back to attention.

"The Brit is diving. He can't get that Kraut off his tail!" Patrick exclaimed. "Come on! Get away! Full throttle!" Patrick yelled. "Look at that. The second Brit is diving towards the Kraut that's following the other Brit. Get him!"

More gunfire shot out from the German plane as Patrick said, "Watch out! Watch out!"

Earl thought he sounded like an announcer at a baseball game. A very excited announcer.

"Look, the Brit is pulling up again." There was more gunfire, this time from the second Brit. "Bloody Hell!" Patrick screamed. "He missed him!"

The German plane angled itself in the opposite direction of the first British plane. All the soldiers were transfixed. All 183 U.S. Army helmets pointed towards the sky. They cheered for the Brits. They cursed at the Krauts.

"Why do they call it a dogfight?" Earl asked, confused by the term.

"When a plane goes into a steep turn, the engine can quit. So a pilot can turn off his engine to avoid a stall. When he starts the engine again, it makes a sound like a dog barking," Patrick explained.

"I get it. That's a dogfight. Wow!" Earl said. "What are they doing now? They stopped chasing."

"It looks like they're out of ammunition. A Brit plane and . . . looks like one of the Kraut planes must be going back to their camp. Well, they didn't shoot each other down. Guess they'll live to fight another day," Patrick said.

"So it's over?" Earl asked.

Patrick studied the sky for a moment. He looked at the British plane. Then he looked at the German plane. There was quite a distance between them, and some of the clouds looked like they were between them. Earl wondered if they purposely tried to hide in the clouds. Each plane was just coming out of a wide upward arc. Both were now flying level.

"You're not going to believe what you are about to see," Patrick said. He talked fast, his announcing voice sounded very excited.

"What? What are they going to do?" Earl asked.

"See how they've lined up? They are going to fly straight at each other. If the Brit gets lucky and clips the Kraut plane just right, it will knock him out of the sky," Patrick said excitedly.

A chill ran up Earl's back. His mouth fell open as he thought about the courage one must have to fly a plane straight at an enemy. *Oh God! Would one of the planes dive at the last minute?* He was unsure if he could watch. But he couldn't look away. He had to see how it would turn out. Patrick began his announcing.

"Steady you Brit! Steady!" he yelled.

The British plane's wings moved back and forth on a straight course. It headed directly for the German plane. The German pilot kept the wings of his plane still. They were closing in on the distance from each other.

"I can't believe this. Look at them. Headed straight for each other," Earl said, as he raised his arm. He wanted his arm well placed so he could cover his eyes quickly if he decided he couldn't take watching the planes crash into each other. He envisioned a giant explosion in the sky and flaming pieces of the planes falling to earth. Some of the soldiers yelled at the planes, their fists or rifles raised in the air. Others were stiff and so still they weren't even blinking.

"Okay, this is it. Neither pilot is changing course. Who's going to win this fight? Come on you Brit," Patrick said as he clenched his teeth.

Earl knew the planes were going to run straight into each other. He couldn't believe he was witnessing this. A dogfight. How would he describe this in a letter to his folks? How would he describe the incredible crash in the sky about to happen?

The planes were now about 30 feet apart. The German pilot angled the wings of his plane sharply at the British. Earl heard the clash of wings. The German had timed his move perfectly. His right wing smashed into the right wing of his opponent. Debris from each plane flew into the sky. Earl saw that the wings on each plane were damaged. Some of the supporting pieces that held the wings together were missing. Wood fell from the sky.

The German pilot gained control quickly as he leveled his wings and flew on a straight course again. Earl swallowed hard. He watched as the British plane flipped completely over. It was at an odd angle and seemed to hang in the sky. The British pilot struggled to gain control of his plane. Earl gripped his rifle. He needed something to hold onto. Remarkably, the British pilot leveled the wings on his plane and both continued to fly in a straight line away from each other.

"The fight's over," Patrick advised Earl.

Earl took a deep breath. He realized he had been holding it as he watched the planes on their collision course.

"We can only hope that Brit gets the Kraut next time," Patrick said. He stepped towards the train to help finish unloading the equipment.

Earl wiped the sweat from his forehead.

The men unloaded the equipment and carried it through some woods until they reached a small creek where they were to build a pontoon bridge. The officer in charge, Major Cummings, had ordered them to dig along the bank of the creek. One side had a large overhanging area that could collapse under the weight of a vehicle. He had wanted them to slant the embankment away from the creek, but that area needed to be removed before the pontoon bridge was constructed. The major warned the enlisted men to avoid standing under the embankment so it wouldn't cave in on them. The excavation seemed to be going well. Then, it happened in a flash.

A huge chunk of the overhanging ground fell. Morgan and another soldier were buried under a pile of heavy mud. Morgan was face down under several cubic yards of it, unable to move. His right leg was twisted at an unnatural angle. He inhaled muddy water and could do nothing to move his arms or free himself.

Morgan's mind raced. He had survived army training camp. He had survived influenza. This was his first day in the field. Probably his last. To die in France! In a muddy grave. So far from his home in Michigan. To end up in a French cemetery. To die from an accident and not a German bullet. *Oh Lord!*

Earl was six feet away. The jolt of the avalanche of mud knocked him down. He was sprawled out in water that was about four feet deep. The creek was ice cold. He was soaked through and through. He managed to push himself up and stand in the water. His clothes felt like they weighed 200 pounds.

The force of the mud caused the frogs to erupt in a wild frenzy. Instantly, there were thousands of large, slimy frogs, thrashing and splashing. Water and mud flew furiously. Earl looked at the avalanche of mud and the surreal storm of frogs. He could see a leg sticking out of the pile of mud—he knew it was Morgan's.

Earl scrambled towards the mud. Men yelled. Frogs seemingly attacked. He was hitting at the frogs as he slogged through mud and water to his friend. He grabbed a shovel and drove it into the mud with his foot. He knew he only had a very short time to help dig Morgan out. Earl scooped up a huge clot of mud with his shovel; when he tried to throw it off, the heavy mud just stuck to it. He stared at the shovel in panic because of the amount of time it was taking to uncover the men, when a giant frog leaped and hit him square in the face. The sky appeared to be raining great quantities of frogs. Earl spit mud out of his mouth and struggled again to scrape it off the shovel.

It was like heavy clay. It refused to come off. Some started to claw at the mud with their bare hands. Patrick had an axe that he pounded into the pile of mud. The axe stuck, and with both hands he pulled it out. A giant glob of mud was attached. This was mud like nothing he had ever seen. He realized their digging could injure Morgan even more, so he threw his shovel aside: "Boys! Use your hands or you're going to drive your shovels right into his spine!" He dug furiously into the giant pile of mud as frogs pelted him from every angle.

Major Cummings had remained on high ground. Earl was angry they hadn't listened to his warning. Now they may have lost two of them in a mudslide. They should've had the bridge up by now. The sight of the soldiers in the mud and the muck was alarming. The hoard of frogs leaping and fighting to get away was unbelievable.

The major determined that his engineers needed direction. Reluctantly, he started across the creek. Fighting frogs. *Unbelievable!* "Lads! Uncover their heads first," he yelled as the frogs attacked him, having no consideration for rank. "We need to get them breathing. Then we can figure out how to get the mud off of them. They first need to breathe!"

After a few moments of furious mud digging, the boys uncovered Morgan's head, and he began coughing and spitting mud. The rest of his body was still under the heavy weight of mud. He struggled for air. Earl tried to keep the frogs from hitting his face. Morgan couldn't move his arms yet. He worked to get air in his lungs. His body felt like a giant vise was squeezing it. At least now he was breathing. Earl and the other soldiers worked to uncover the rest of him, pulling him from the muddy grave.

"Bring him up here, lads!" Major Cummings ordered.

Making their way to higher ground to escape the onslaught of frogs, Earl and a few others carried Morgan up the embankment. They dropped him. And then dropped him again. Everything was slippery from mud.

"Bloody Hell!" yelled the major. "The man barely survives being buried to death. Now you drop him? Are you trying to break his neck? Hold onto him!"

The muddy tangle of proud American Expeditionary Force engineers finally carried Morgan to safety. Earl sat on the ground next to him, and held Morgan erect while he pounded on his back, trying to get mud out of his throat. Morgan groaned as he leaned against Earl and saw his leg. Something wasn't right. His leg was angled upward. He reached down to feel it, as if his eyes were deceiving him.

"We need to get him some medical help, Major," Earl said breathlessly.

"We're too far away from camp, lads. The train won't be back until later," Major Cummings said.

"We have to do something to help him!" Earl protested.

The major kneeled by Morgan and tapped along both sides of his leg to make an assessment. He scratched his head and pulled on one ear, and stood up and crossed his arms, deep in thought. He kneeled by Morgan again, started to place his hands on Morgan's leg, then abruptly stopped.

Major Cummings stood up and, tugging on his ear again, looked at Morgan thoughtfully. "Hold him down lads. I saw a leg injury like this once on a polo field."

With Morgan restrained, the major grabbed his leg with both hands. He gave the leg a twist right and then a twist left. Then right again. Morgan's knee gave a loud popping sound and went back to its rightful place in his socket. Words rarely uttered in his home state of Michigan gushed forth from Morgan in a torrent.

"Maybe he would have been happier if we'd left him under that pile of mud," said Major Cummings.

"I'm sure he's very appreciative Major. He's just showing us how much he paid attention to those navy sailors while we were crossing the pond," Earl said.

The soldiers expected Major would call it a day. They were muddy, wet, exhausted. The frogs had unnerved them, let alone almost losing two soldiers to mud. But Major Cummings thought differently. With Morgan's leg back in place, he ordered the men to complete the bridge. Of course, they did as ordered, but many soldiers used several of Morgan's choice words as they constructed the pontoon bridge.

On the way back to camp, Morgan leaned over to Earl and said, "Guess you'll have something to write about tonight to the folks back home."

19

American Crusaders

Pvt. Earl Young
401 Ponton Park Engineers
Camp Upton, New York
Somewhere in France
Oct. 20, 1918

Dear folks at home,
    *Well, maybe you have been wondering why that promised
letter never reached you, but please excuse me because I have been
feeling as tho I didn't care for anything since Sept 30.*
    *First I was sea sick and then I got the Influenza and thank
God you wasn't with me, for all the vomiting for 2 or 3 days then
began the coughing & spitting. The hospital was so full where we
landed I decided it best to stay clear of it. We were soon transferred
and I immediately went to a hospital where we could be cared for.
Well, I feel my own self again and on my feet.*
    *Will join my company again in a few days. I am eating like a
hog & the cough is all gone so don't worry for by the time you get
this I will be as hardy as ever.*

We crossed the Atlantic in 8 days in the largest ship in the world. The most treacherous thing we saw on the boat was several large whales. The gunners make short work of them. The noise the boat makes reminds me of a lumber wagon on a frozen road. It is 950 feet long. Some boat.

It is an old saying to speak "Sunny France" but it has been raining 2 days out of 5 since I landed here. France looks very much like Virginia. It is nearly all hills, rocks and trees. The farmers have very fine looking little gardens. They have the patches all fenced of like the stump ground there at home. They string their five horses out all in the furrow and use walking plows. The horses are all nice large ones.

We traveled in box cars but could get a fair idea of the country as we passed through the country. I know of a lot of things to say but must wait until I get back.

We have a nice bunch of boys & officers so things are very much more agreeable in camp.

Well I guess it is closing time.

I might suggest that you put a sweater or heavy jersey in that Xmas package. A helmet cap too.

Also you had better send this on to Mabel & then to Geo. because I don't know when I will write again. News is so scarce.

Answer soon.

Your sammy son,

Private Earl Young
401 Pontoon Park Engineers
American Expeditionary Forces
Via N.Y.

The Omaha World Herald

July 7, 1918

The U.S. Army reports today that fighting on the French front turned in favor of the U.S. and its allies. The Kaiser of Germany, in attempt to thwart the oncoming rush of American troops, has launched a Spring Offensive. The German offensive was unsuccessful and Germany's Stormtroopers made insignificant gains. The U.S. Army faulted the German preparation for battle as lacking clear cut goals. The British and American troops pushed all German advances back with their superior cavalry units.

Morgan was back in the hospital. His leg was now in a splint and he was forced to keep it elevated. The field trip had exhausted Earl and he was beginning to get sick. Again. Being in the rain and getting soaked through and through had given him the chills and his fever had returned. A doctor gave him orders to rest and sent him to the hospital. He advised Earl to fully recover before he went back out to the field again.

October 23, 1918

Dear Brother & Family,

I have been in this country about 16 days but didn't find courage to write before. I have just survived a week in a hospital, but will be out in a day or two now.

The second of the 8 days on the boat I got sea sick and while still so weak got the Influenza. Have suffered the same ever since. I feel much stronger now and can eat just as hardy as ever. I have lost all the fat I gained in the States. They take good care of a fellow over here so why should I worry!

This country looks just as one would imagine that Missouri looks like. "Get my dutch"?

The ocean was calm all the way over & the ship didn't rock much but imagine yourself inside the old Port Huron at top speed. Just the noise. The ship is the longest afloat. 950 feet long. 100 feet wide. Some boat. Would hold all the people of Sidney and still not be crowded.

We had quite a frost the other night and is making the leaves fall as the warm sun is out today as it seldom is. It's all raining here.

Must close & go to chow. Paper is scarce. So is envelope.

Your Brother
401 Ponton Park Engineers
American Exped. Forces
Via N.Y.

Ans. soon.

Is Ed drafted yet? Write all the news and then some? Don't delay. I have carried this paper clear from Ga. So don't scold the fellow as I'm writing this on my knee.

Earl didn't know that the doctors at the hospital had given him a 60 percent chance of dying, and now he thinks about how influenza could have killed him as easily as inhaling a chemical on the battlefield. He wondered if he would have coughed as violently had he breathed the deadly chloride gas. He wondered if his lungs would have ached any worse if the burning chemicals had filled his lungs. Earl had had strange thoughts when the influenza was at its worst. He thought a lot about that life insurance policy. As he lay on his cot resting, trying ever so hard not to cough—only to cough over and over again—he thought more about this incident.

He found out later that the insurance agent had signed his name without his knowledge. George and Laura had often told him to be careful when he went to Sidney. The town was filled to the brim with crooks and had that kind of reputation. Fifty years ago, in the 1860s and 1870s, it was a dangerous place. You had to watch people carefully, and its reputation wasn't any better in 1918. Earl had obviously been getting a lesson in life from an unethical Sidney businessman. He thought about how ironic it would be to die in France from influenza. Many soldiers had. The insurance agent would have to pay the $2000 if he died. The thought made him smile.

"Are you from Nebraska?" a soldier in the next cot asked.

"I'm from Brock. Name's Earl." They shook hands.

"I grew up in Palmer, Nebraska. Charles Mangelsen."

"Glad to meet you. And to think I had to come all the way to France to meet someone else from Nebraska," Earl laughed. "I'm recovering from the Spanish flu but the worst is behind me." He tried to stifle a cough but was unsuccessful.

"Well, you're not alone, Earl. A number of soldiers from my regiment had the flu. My family in Palmer tells me that the flu there was so widespread that schools were closed," Charles said.

"That's what I've heard too. Schools, churches, offices have all had to close because it's so contagious," Earl added.

"I haven't had the flu but, unfortunately during my field artillery training this morning, a cannon misfired and a piece of it hit my shoulder. I had to have a little surgery to remove it. I'll be out in a few days and if the war isn't over, I'll join my artillery unit," Charles said, as he adjusted the splint that was holding up his left arm.

"It's too bad we're in the hospital but it sure is good to find someone I can talk Nebraskan to," Charles said and laughed.

Earl swallowed water to suppress his cough, then said, "Well, I know this is something you can relate to. Many of the soldiers I talk to think Nebraska is just a flat prairie where buffalo still thunder from one end of the state to the other, with no trees and no rivers and—"

"Still has Indians and farmers fighting!" Charles interrupted.

Earl nodded his head in agreement.

The next few hours Earl and Charles were rapidly discussing how their lives were intertwined with Nebraska and France. Charles talked about swimming and fishing in the Loup River and how ironic the word Loup is French for wolf. The boys compared stories learned in school about how some of the first explorers in Nebraska were French. A French adventurer named Etienne Veniard de Bourgmond was the first to record the name Nebraska in his journals. He discovered that the Platte River drained into the Missouri, and determined that the Indians described the Platte using the word Nebraska, meaning flat water. They talked about how pioneers on the Oregon Trail described the Platte as a mile wide and an inch deep. Earl talked about the Lewis and Clark Expedition that camped at the mouth of the Little Nemaha River, not too far from his hometown of Brock. Since the United States did not own the territory west of the Missouri, they needed permission from France prior to the expedition.

"Well, I never imaged I would be in France talking to a fellow Nebraskan about the French influence on our home state," Charles said.

"I guess it's just another reason to be a proud soldier in the army, doing our bit to help pay back the Frenchies for putting Nebraska on the map," Earl said.

He was so excited to be talking Nebraskan he had entirely forgotten about coughing.

"Want to play checkers? My friend Morgan usually beats me so maybe I could try my luck playing someone else," Earl said.

"I still have one good arm, so I could manage a game," Charles said.

"Before we start, I need to get this letter in the mail. I haven't written my family in two weeks since I felt so bad. I'm sure they're getting concerned they haven't heard from me," Earl said.

"That's fine. I have a postcard I need to mail too," Charles said.

Possession of Margaret Iler Davis, who grew up in Palmer, Nebraska. The postcard was addressed to Beatrice Nicholas. Their families were close friends.

France
1918

    Saving a little time this afternoon and thought I would send
you a few lines to let you know I am O.K. and am hoping you
are the same. I heard that the Spanish Flu is also in the States.
I hope none of you have had it and that the schools are opened
again soon. We have been very busy here, finished the training this
morning. The weather is nice & warm. I must close, hoping you
will ans. soon.

I remain yours,
Cpl. Charles F. Mangelsen
Batry C 338 F.A. A.E.F

Soldiers Mail
Earl Young
U.S. Army
Somewhere in France
Oct. 28, 1918

Dear Bro. & Family,
    Just had dinner & a dose of, well don't know what it was but it
didn't taste good. It sorta kills the cough tho. I haven't received any
mail since I landed here, tho it has been 20 days since I have seen
my company now. My mind sorta seems to run astray today so don't
get excited if I get some Virginia expressions mixed up in this letter.
    I am feeling fine these days once again so that accounts for it I
presume. Possibly because of the sign written on the bulletin board
here in front of that reads:

> *According to official wire*
> *hostilities between allies and*
> *Germany suspend at 5 p.m.*
> *November 6, 1918*

Altho it is signed by a Captain, it seems allmost too good to be true. I think I will be just as willing to hit Cheyenne Co. as I was to leave it. Still I'm not kicking.

Sure would like to know whether Edw. is drafted or not. I guess he would make a good soldier all right, but don't imagine he would like it at all. One has got to like it, take it from me.

Maybe I can write better now. A Y.M.C.A. man just gave me a package of gum. I have been broke for 2 mo. so can appreciate all gifts and gladly return the thanks. Our company has never had a pay day since it was organized in mid Sept. sometime.

We get good appetizing food all the time so you see one don't crave for the grapes, nuts & apples & lemons as one would if the grub wasn't good.

I have been in a hospital most of the time, not in bed and still not able to get out and work. The Influenza cough you till you all weak. Is there much of it in the States?

What do you do for a living now? Still got that ½ section of hills yet? Maybe they aren't hills but I have a broad imagination. (See!)

Do you ever see anybody I know?

I spend most of my time playing checkers, dominoes, indoor tennis, reading papers & magazines, coughing in between times.

Will try and eat 4th of July dinner with you. (Maybe one or two before). (See.) Write often to Your Bro.,

Earl
401 Ponton Park Engrs.
American Expeditionary Forces

possibly, because of the sign written on the bulletin ~~bort~~ board here in front of me that reads:

According to official wire hostalaties between allies and Germany suspend at 5 P.M. November 6, 1918.

Altho it is signed by a captain, It seems allmost too good to be true.

I think I will be just as willing to hit Cheyenne Co. as I was to leave it. Still I'm not kicking.

Sure would like to know whether Edw. is drafted or not. I guess he would make a good

"Morgan! Did you see the message printed on the bulletin board?" asked Earl with excitement in his voice.

"No—I can't get around too good with this splint on my leg, you know," said Morgan.

"It says that hostilities between us and Germany will end on November 6!"

"Yahoo!" yelled Morgan.

"You can say that again. In fact, I'll say it with you," Earl said. "YAHOO!"

"What are we going to do to celebrate?" Morgan asked.

"I just found out that we're going to have a special show tonight," Earl said.

"I sure would like to go to that but with this injured leg of mine I won't be able to. I hope you'll come by tomorrow and tell me all about it," Morgan said. The hospital bed was getting drab and lonely.

"I'll do better than that. I'll take you."

"How are you going to do that?" Earl asked.

"I'll just sweet talk one of the nurses here and ask to borrow a wheelchair for a few hours, load you up, and figure out a way to get you there."

"You are a true blue pal. That's just great."

"Be right back," Earl said.

Any entertainment for the boys was greatly appreciated. Generally a great deal of thought was given to presenting the entertainment so it would be excellent. Tonight the show would have to be extraordinary because the war was ending. The absolute best that could be arranged. And it was. The boys were not disappointed. It was the best show the American Expeditionary Force had ever seen.

Earl and Morgan talked for days afterwards about the overpowering performance given by Anastasie and Adrienne Dubois. Those Dubois sisters were beautiful. Their dresses were elegant. Their voices, powerful and heavenly. The sisters were incredibly popular in French society and their performance at the Bouffes-Parisiens had been canceled, so they could perform for the Yanks. They sang a song about a baby's prayer for her dad Over There—when they finished, there wasn't a dry eye in the camp.

"Just a Baby's Prayer at Twilight"
Song lyrics by Sam M. Lewis, music by M. K. Jerome; 1918

I've heard the pray'rs of mothers,
Some of them old and gray.
I've heard the pray'rs of others,
For those who went away.
Oft times a pray'r will teach one,
The meaning of goodbye.
I felt the pain of each one,
But this one made me cry:

Just a baby's pray'r at twilight,
When lights are low.
Poor baby's years,
Are filled with tears.
There's a mother there at twilight
Who's proud to know,
Her precious little tot,
Is Dad's forget-me-not.
After saying "Goodnight Mama,"
She climbs upstairs,
Quite unawares,
And says her pray'rs.

"Oh! Kindly tell my daddy that he must take care!"
That's a baby's pray'r at twilight,
For her daddy, "over there."

The gold that some folks pray for,
Brings nothing but regrets.
Someday this gold won't pay for,
Their many lifelong debts.
Some pray'rs may be neglected,
Beyond the Golden Gates.
But when they're all collected,
Here's one that never waits.

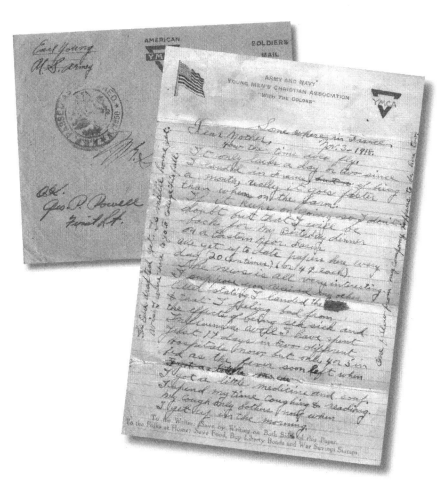

Earl Young
U.S. Army
Somewhere in France
Nov. 3, 1918

Dear Mother,

How the time does fly. It only lacks a day or two since I landed in France, of being a month. Really it goes faster than when on the farm. If it keeps on going so I don't doubt but that I will be back for my birthday dinner on a Eastern Nebr. farm.

We get up to date papers here every day (20 centimes) (or 4 cents each). The news is all very interesting. I suppose you received my other letter stating I landed the ▮▮▮▮ & that I was feeling bad from the effects of being sea sick and Influenza. Well I have spent just 17 days in two different hospital now, but only 4 or 5 in bed as the fever soon left when I got a little medicine and soup.

I spend my time coughing & reading. My cough only bothers now when I get up in the morning. We are furnished with all kinds of books & magazines so there is a big assortment to select from. Some of the fellows, back from the "Front" can tell bushels of interesting stories, all welcomed to the ear. Sometimes a bunch of boys will be sitting round, telling what they intend to do when they get back. And so the time goes.

I haven't done a lick of work or training since I landed so you see I am anxious to get back to my company so I won't miss so much. I hope I will get a truck to drive as from what I hear I think I would like that best.

Hoping that you get this by Thanksgiving and please don't worry about me for I am feeling the part of a man again and will not know that I was on the bum by the time you get this.

Please, look up all the addresses of the boys from around there that crossed the pond & send them. I might be very close & get to see some of them if I only knew it. See. Send full addresses.

Answer soon & often,

Your son
Private Earl Young
401 Ponton Park Engineers
American E.F.

Can you imagine it? I haven't had a haircut for 2 mo. and haven't had a pay day yet. It will be another mo. now for fuzzy head. Ha

Rice and apricots vanilla flavor, roast beef, cabbage & carrots, coffee & bread for supper. We always get white bread 3 times a day, 2 slices usually. I like cabbage & carrots now. Wish I had my pipe here. Tobacco is issued but can't go it anymore.

Is Ed drafted yet. Is Millie home yet. Wish I was there to go to College this fall.

One of the fellows from my company happens to be here too.

GOOD-BYE FRANCE

"Goodbye France"
A song by Irving Berlin, 1918

I can picture the boys "over there,"
Making plenty of noise "over there."
And if I'm not wrong, it won't be long
Ere a certain song will fill the air.
It's all very clear the time's drawing near
When they'll be marching down to the pier, singing:

Goodbye France,
We'd love to linger longer,
But we must go home.
Folks are waiting
To welcome us
Across the foam.
We were glad to stand
Side by side with you,
Mighty proud
To have died with you.
So goodbye France,
You'll never be forgotten by the U.S.A.

They are waiting for one happy day
When the word comes to start on their way.
With a tear-dimmed eye, they'll say goodbye,
But their hearts will cry, hip-hip hooray.
The friends that they made will wish that they stayed,
As they start on their homeward parade, singing.

Cover up each cough and sneeze. If you don't you'll spread disease.

20

Special Pink

There was army life. And then there was everyone else's life. Earl wrote letters from France to Nebraska. His family wrote to him. Letters were shared and forwarded on to other family members. A shared letter in the family was good but a letter addressed to you was even better. Earl's sisters took offense if the letters were not specifically addressed to them often enough. *Sisters! Oh boy!*

Millie was still in Dalton helping George and Laura with their new baby. Families helped each other, especially when a new baby arrived. The Spanish flu was a worry everywhere. Adults and children of all ages were affected. Sometimes their cases were mild, other times it was severe. Not everyone survived. A number of family members in the Young family contracted the flu. Or severe colds. Or the grippe. Sometimes it was difficult to tell what it was.

Dalton, Nebraska
Nov. 15, 1918

Dear Folks at home,
Laura got your letter yesterday afternoon but isn't quite able to answer yet so I am writing instead. I don't feel much like writing

when the letters aren't addressed to me once in a while at least. Tho't you all had dropped off the earth or gone to war you never wrote for so long. Got a letter from Earl yesterday too and will enclose it. It's the first we got of him since he sent the card he arrived over there. You never said if he sent you one too or not.

I guess everybody here is over the flu now. Geo. still has some cold and keeps sneezing. Laura's cold and grippe stayed with her till yesterday. She began to feel better and has entirely left today.

She & baby Hazel Laura Young are getting along fine otherwise. We were afraid baby would take the cold from Laura but a little hoarseness was all it effected her but is OK now and sleeps biggest share of the time. If she didn't I don't know how I ever could get along with the work.

There's no one extra here but the work is here and it takes all of my time somehow. I never had the flu, as they call it, half as bad as the rest here and only half as long. I take special pink pretty regular. I think that's all that made the difference. Ask Dr. Fletcher if he don't think so.

We read about the war and peace celebrating in the Omaha Daily News but further than that we hear nor see nothing out here in this prairie land.

They say the wheat crop looks dandy, the best ever, can say that much for this country.

Don't suppose Ed went to camp last Tuesday from what the papers say. One don't get the Auburn Herald until on Mondays.

Geo. is painting the grainary now days. Tomorrow I guess he intends to scout around for a milk cow. This one is nearly dry.

You never said where you got your cow but I bet you paid a big price for her. Cows out here at one sale sold for $140 for one and $180 for the other.

Geo. traded his big Mitchell on a Dodge, now he thinks there's nothing better than a Dodge.

I don't know of anything more so good night.

Write soon to Millie

No, we never received any Xmas parcel present from Earl.

The Omaha World Herald

October 4, 1918

Today the Omaha Health Commissioner, Dr. E. T. Manning, issued a public health order closing churches, schools, movie houses and other places of congregation in the city. The order came a day after an out-break of 30 cases of the influenza epidemic at Fort Omaha. He hoped the closure order would limit the ability for the public to intermingle and spread the disease. Orders included refraining from using common drinking cups or kissing. Theatre managers were outraged. The Brandeis Theater expected to lose $4500 on its upcoming performance of "Marry in Haste."

As the disease continued to spread, even with the restrictions, more orders were given. Outdoor gatherings including parades, church services, public funerals, and patriotic meetings were banned. But after learning of the ban on outdoor activities, the athletic director of Creighton University announced that the upcoming football game against their foremost rivals would be played as scheduled. The game against Lincoln Cotner College went on, as did the other football games. It was not until October 22 that the Nebraska Board of Health issued a statewide closure order regarding a ban on all groups of twelve or more people.

The Nebraska Board of Health lifted the closure order on November 1, 1918. Residents of Nebraska were thrilled. Theater owners reopened. The Gayety Theater held a special performance one minute after midnight on the morning of the closure order. Department stores held sales. Schools reopened. Almost immediately, new influenza cases and deaths spiked. Reluctant to reissue a ban on activities, the Board of Health delayed. They distributed leaflets with the phrase "Cover up each cough and sneeze; if you don't you'll spread disease."

The influenza cases continued to rise, unabated. A hospital in Omaha reported over 400 new cases in a single day. The state made anti-pneumonia vaccine doses available to doctors. They later found the doctors were charging over $10 per dose. Homes were placed under quarantine. There were still 1200 deaths by the end of the year. The influenza epidemic in Omaha was one of the most severe in the nation.

The cycle of life went on. Babies were born in Nebraska. Soldiers died on front lines in France. The Spanish flu was spreading death everywhere. Doctors used whatever medical training they had to fight the flu. Dr. Fletcher, M.D., a graduate of the Creighton University of Medicine and prestigious alum, pressured the school to allow Creighton to play their annual football game against Cotner College. After all, he had tickets to the big event, and had already invited a special female friend to the game.

He had a busy practice of many things: delivering babies, appendectomy surgeries, hemorrhoid removals; he prescribed medications for colds, warts, and headaches; he set broken arms. He did it all. And when the influenza hit, it provided a big boom for his practice. He went from working 10 hours a day to 22. He saw sick people with the flu until he fell asleep. Sometimes he fell asleep even while standing. The state gave him free anti-pneumonia vaccine. The doctor was an important man though. His time was valuable. It didn't seem unreasonable to him to charge his patients $17 a dose. He was helping them and, therefore, should be grateful. They were pressured to buy Special Pink—for their own general, good health; after all, Dr. Fletcher was a professional. He prescribed different medications for the flu, depending on the patient's symptoms. Usually though, the good doctor prescribed Special Pink.

Special Pink was his invention for recovering from the flu. Or a cold. Grippe. Or whatever. He would tell his patients it works. If they believed him, indeed it worked. If a patient still got sick, even after using Special Pink, Dr. Fletcher would simply say they didn't come to him soon enough. Or he would up the dose. Or tell them to put a poultice of onion root on their chest. Or drink a cup of chamomile tea just before taking Special Pink.

When Special Pink helped a patient, Dr. Fletcher would advise them to continue the medicine. It could be deadly if discontinued too soon. He would be happy to be of assistance in getting them all they needed. He was the only one who had it. Special Pink could be shipped anywhere. He had patients all over Nebraska, Kansas, Iowa, and Missouri who owed their life to the good Dr. Fletcher.

His patients referred to him as the best doctor between Chicago and Denver. He was certainly on a first name basis with his banker, who also took Special Pink and was careful to take it three times a day. He had it for breakfast with a brandy chaser. He took it for lunch with a quaff of stout. He swallowed it for supper with two shots of whiskey. His system was obviously working. He not only thwarted the influenza, he hardly ever sneezed.

The cycle of life went on.

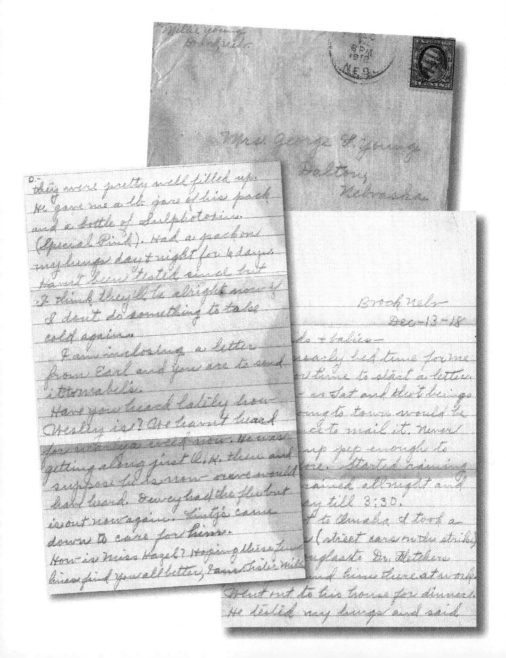

Millie Young
Brock, Nebr.
Dec 13, 1918

Dear kids & babies,

   It's nearly bedtime for me and a poor time to start a letter.
Tomorrow is Sat. and that beings they are going to town. Would
be a good chance to mail it. Never mustered up pep enough to
write before. Started raining yesterday. Rained all night and all
day till 3:30.

   When I got to Omaha I took a jitney bus (street cars on the
strike) to 10th & Douglas to Dr. Fletcher's factory. Found him
there at work. Went out to his house for dinner. He tested my
lungs and said they were pretty well filled up. He gave me a lb.
jar of his pack and a bottle of Sulphotoxin. (Special pink). Had
a pack on my lungs day & night for 6 days. Haven't been tested
since but I think they'll be alright now if I don't do something to
take cold again.

   I am enclosing a letter from Earl and you are to send it to
Mabel's.

   Have you heard lately how Wesley is? We haven't heard for
nearly a week now. He was getting along just o.k. then and suppose he is now—or we would have heard. Dewey had the flu but is
out now again. Linty's came down to care for him.

   How is Miss Hazel? Hoping these few lines find you all better,
I am.

Sister Millie

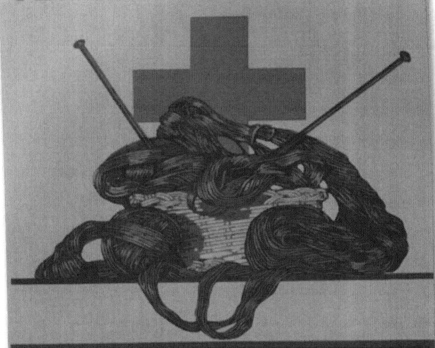

21

Knit a Bit

The war was over—but the waiting to go home was not. Earl thought he would surely be home for Christmas. Or at least parading on Broadway in New York City. But here it was Christmas Eve. He hadn't felt a more lonely feeling than being away from his family on this night. This was the first Christmas he wouldn't enjoy Mother's traditional roast goose with plum marinade. He was sad, a little. But he knew all too well that things could've been worse, a whole lot worse. He was forever grateful he had recovered from the flu and regained his health.

Earl's only job now was to wait for an available ship to take him back. Across the pond. The army would tell him when it was time to board—eventually. So there really wasn't much to kick about. Even Morgan had guard duty so there would be no checkers game on Christmas Eve. To keep him occupied, Earl read a book of poems written by Alfred Lord Tennyson that Morgan had given him. He opened the book to the last poem.

"Crossing the Bar"
A poem by Alfred Lord Tennyson, 1889

Sunset and evening star,
And one clear call for me!
And may there be no moaning of the bar,
When I put out to sea,

But such a tide as moving seems asleep,
Too full for sound and foam,
When that which drew from out the boundless deep
Turns again home.

Twilight and evening bell,
And after that the dark!
And may there be no sadness of farewell,
When I embark;

For tho' from out our bourne of Time and Place
The flood may bear me far,
I hope to see my Pilot face to face
When I have crost the bar.

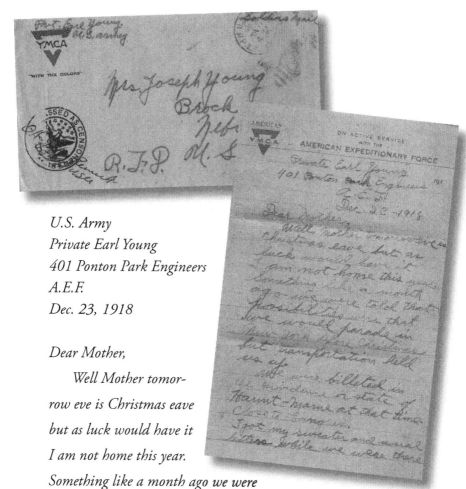

U.S. Army
Private Earl Young
401 Ponton Park Engineers
A.E.F.
Dec. 23, 1918

Dear Mother,

    Well Mother tomor-
row eve is Christmas eave
but as luck would have it
I am not home this year.
Something like a month ago **we were**
told that possibilities were that we would parade in New York for
Christmas but transportation held us up.

    We were billeted in the Providence or state of Haunt-Marne
at that time. Close to Langres.

    I got my sweater and several letters while we were there.

    We have been moved about a week now. Billeted close to
Nancey now. Not so very far from the coast because the tide comes
in everyday on the river here. The weather is real warm here. The
grass is still green. There is several palm trees around in front. The

gardens are green too. It rains nearly every day but hardly cold enough for a overcoat.

I got 3 or foure letters here already. I don't know much to write but this will let you know that I am well and that I figure on beating this letter to you but in case I don't I will be there soon afterwards anyway. We come on the first available ship. I guess. That can't be to soon because I want to see little Hazel.

Sure was glad to hear that Edd. wasn't called at all.

Well, writing by candle light don't go good and I have been shoveling mud all day so will go to bed shortly I guess. Reveille at 6:30 in the morning. Breakfast at 6:45. It isn't very light then yet. It seems as tho the sun comes up in the west here.

One of the fellows just brought some candy. 10 franks or $2 for 3 bars of chocolate. Not sweet at that. I haven't had a pay-day yet as it happens. 5 months spot cash coming to me (Bucco Mone).

Must close and write to Geo. & Mabel.

As ever Your son,
Private Earl Young
401 Ponton Park Engrs.
A.E.F.

When Earl first joined the army, he had written several letters asking his mother to send him a sweater. His first request was in September. The evenings were cool and some days the rain would make you cold the entire day. The army provided them uniforms but the uniforms didn't provide much warmth. In October and November the need for a sweater increased and Earl wrote again asking for one. For Earl, he just wanted to be warm and wondered what was taking so long.

Earl's mother had been working on the sweater and wasn't able to spend as much time knitting it as she would have liked. There were just so many things to take care of during the day in order to keep the rest of the family fed and clothed. She would work on it every night. She had read in the paper that there was a great need for sweaters, hats, and socks for the troops. Some towns formed 'Wool Brigades' and considered knitting a patriotic duty.

The article in the paper described a three-day knitting bee in Central Park, a drive to produce wool clothing to send to the troops. There was such a massive turn out it was difficult to talk because the clacking of knitting needles was so loud—other knitting bees began organizing in states all across America.

The article had so inspired Earl's mother that her nightly knitting seemed to be more efficient than it was. The next day, she ordered more wool yarn from the Betsy Ross Yarn Mills. She liked that they advertised their wool to be water repellent and a gray color. Their slogan was "Uncle Sam Wants You to Knit to Protect His Boys Over There."

Mrs. Joseph Young became part of the wool brigade and was proud of it.

"Knit Your Bit"
A poem in the *Khaki Knitting Book*,
edited by Olive Whiting, 1917

Swiftly, to and fro,
Let your needles fly!
Be not yours to know
Pause, for tear or sigh.

Stitch by stitch they grow,
Garments soft and warm
That will keep life's glow
In some shivering form.

Sweater, muffler, sock,
For the soldiers' wear!
List to pity's knock—
For those "over there."

Children's voices, too,
In the sad refrain,
Wring our hearts anew,
From that world of pain.

Banish for a while
Tints of brighter hue,
Welcome with a smile,
Khaki, gray and blue.

Days are cold and drear,
Nights are long and bleak,
Thoughts from home are dear,
Where the cannons shriek.

Let some simple thing,
That your hand employs,
Cheer and comfort bring
To our gallant Boys.

May there be no end
To what love supplies!
Thus their share we'll send
To our brave Allies!

Pvt. Earl Young
401 Ponton Park
Engrs.
A.E.F.
Jan. 17, 1919

Dear Folks at Home,
I received your letter
10 min. ago dated Dec.
16, 1918 and another
from the west. Good to
know that everyone is
well & happy. I am enjoy-
ing good health myself. I
received that sweater and
have it put to good use. The
Christmas package was sure
fine. French chocolate is
not nearly so sweet.
Your letter of Dec. 6 & Herald paper rec'd last week. Would
like to see them all. Don't know when we will sail but I look for it
soon. I saw a Dutch windmill turning at a distance yesterday.
Glad to hear Mabel is going back to Greenwood. (Mable
may still live there). ha. ha. Don't hesitate to help out the good
work of the Red Cross. It rains every day. Th e sun shines in
between times. Will bring some souvenirs as you ask. Write lots
& often to your son.

Pvt. Earl Young
401 Ponton Park Engineers
A.E.F.

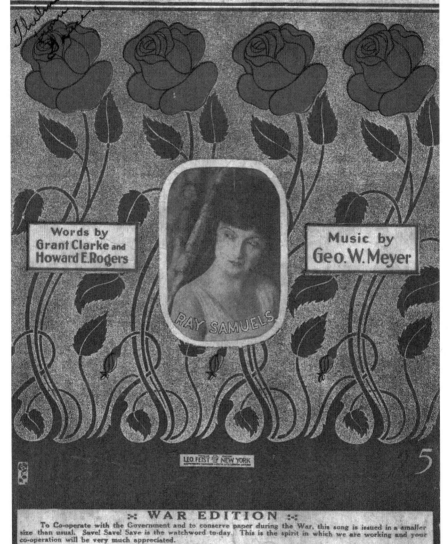

"If He Can Fight Like He Can Love, Good Night Germany"
Song lyrics by Grant Clarke and Howard E. Rogers,
music by George W. Meyer; 1918

Little Mary's beau said, "I've got to go,
I must fight for Uncle Sam."
Standing in the crowd Mary called aloud,
"Fare thee well my lovin' man."
All the girls said, "Ain't he nice and tall."
Mary answered, "Yes, and that's not all."

"If he can fight like he can love,
Oh, what a soldier boy he'll be!
If he's just half as good in a trench
As he was in the park on a bench,
Then ev'ry Hun had better run
And find a great big linden tree.
And if he fights like he can love,
Why, then it's good night Germany!"

Ev'ry single day, all the papers say,
Mary's beau is oh, so brave.
With his little gun, chasing ev'ry Hun,
He has taught them to behave.
Little Mary proudly shakes her head,
And says, "Do you remember what I said?"

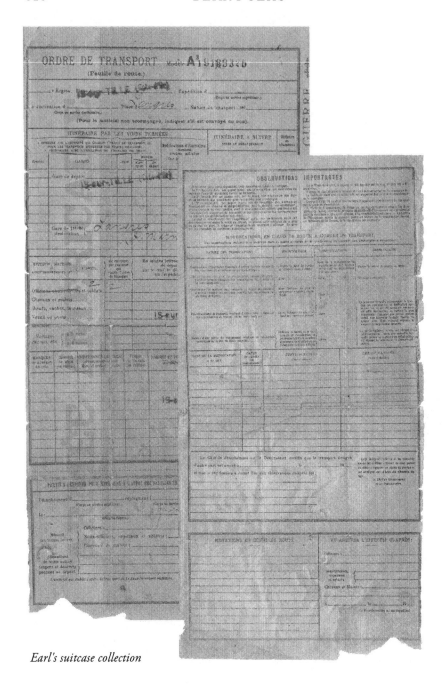

Earl's suitcase collection

Wee, Wee, Marie
(WILL YOU DO ZIS FOR ME)

WORDS BY
ALFRED BRYAN AND
JOE McCARTHY

MUSIC BY
FRED FISHER

McCARTHY & FISHER (INC)
MUSIC PUBLISHERS
224 W 46TH ST. NEW YORK

5

22

Goodbye France

"Wee, Wee, Marie (Will You Do Zis for Me)"
Song lyrics by Alfred Bryan and Joe McCarthy,
music by Fred Fisher; 1918

Poor Johnny's heart went pitty, pitty pat.
Somewhere in sunny France,
He met a girl by chance.
With ze naughty, naughty glance,
She looked just like a kitty, kitty cat.
She loved to dance and play.
Tho' he learned no French when he left the trench,
He knew well enough to say:

Wee, Wee Marie, will you do zis for me?
Wee, Wee Marie, then I'll do zat for you.
I love your eyes; they make me feel so spoony,
You'll drive me looney; you're teasing me.
Why can't we parley-vous like others sweethearts do.
I want a kiss or two from Ma Cherie
Wee, wee Marie, if you'll do zis for me,
Then I'll do zat for you, wee, wee, Marie.

DEAR FOLKS

They walked along the boulevard,
He whispered, "You for me.
Some day in gay Paree,
I will make you marry me."
Just then a bunch of bully, bully boys
Threw kisses on the sly.
Marie got wise when they rolled their eyes;
They sang as they passed her by.

The doughboys had helped defeat Germany. The army had trained pilots, motorcycle dispatchers, cavalry, infantry, and pontoon engineers. They all intermingled onboard the ship to cross the pond back to the U.S.A. They celebrated with slaps on the back and handshakes as they each told stories of their grand adventure in the A.E.F.

"Well Earl, wave goodbye to France," Morgan said.

"Can you believe it? We were only here for five months," Earl said.

"We did what we could to help out," Morgan said. "War isn't just fighting in the trenches."

"That's right. Our war experience was certainly different than others who made it here. We would have done more, given the opportunity. I'm mighty proud of my time in the army," Earl said.

"You and I had quite an adventure, didn't we?"

"There were all kinds of adventures I can share with the people in Nebraska when I get home," Earl said.

"Like how many times I beat you at checkers?" Morgan kidded.

"You mean how many times you got me distracted and squeaked out a win?" Earl kidded back.

"Let's see. While in the army we probably marched twelve thousand miles. We've had reveille at 6:00 almost every morning. We fought the influenza—"

"And barely survived," Earl interrupted.

"We built about as many pontoon bridges for practice as the miles we marched—"

"Which is to say about twelve thousand miles," Earl finished.

"There was that day in French mud," Morgan said. He rubbed his knee, which had instantly started aching.

"I have to admit something, Morgan. I didn't want Major Cummings to pull your knee into place like that," Earl said.

"Why didn't you stop him?" Morgan rubbed his knee a little harder.

"Stop him? He was an officer—I thought he knew what he was doing."

"I'll tell you what. Officer or no officer, the next time someone starts yanking on my leg like that—just stop 'em," Morgan said as he winced.

"Are you going to miss Major Cummings ordering you to do everything all the time?" Earl asked.

"Oh right. It's going to take a while to get out of the habit of waiting for the Major to tell me what to do. Guess I'll have to figure out when to take a drink of water and when to tie my shoes whenever I feel like it," Morgan joked. But he did say one of the best statements I heard in France," Morgan added.

"What's that?" Earl asked. "You may have been happier if we left you buried in the mud?"

"No. The best thing I heard Major Cummings say is"—Morgan cleared his throat to mimic the major: "Well lads, I have news. On the eleventh day, of the eleventh month, at the eleventh hour, Germany will surrender! The war is over! You'll all be home soon."

Morgan offered Earl a new chewing tobacco he was trying out. It was called Peachy Flanders and had a painting of a doughboy holding a beautiful peach in his hand.

"Want a pinch, Earl? You know, just as a medical precaution so you don't contract the Spanish flu again?"

"I'd do almost anything to not go through another round of the flu," Earl said, as he placed some Peachy Flanders in his mouth.

"Maybe it will help with seasickness too," Morgan said hopefully.

"We'll find out soon enough ole buddy." Earl felt the ship start to rock.

"Did you hear about the diplomatic incident about this town?" Morgan asked.

"You mean, about the brothels?

"Yeah, called Maisons Toleree—they're legal in France, you know. So when the A.E.F. made them off limits, it caused a huge economic disaster for the town. It got so bad the Prime Minister of France, Georges Clemenceau, and General Pershing had to get involved. They came up with an alternate plan: medical personnel controlled certain brothels that were specifically for army soldiers," Morgan explained.

"Problem solved, I guess," Earl said.

"There's another interesting part of the story, though, about this whole affair. Forgive the pun," Morgan said and laughed. "When General Pershing's aide presented this alternate plan for approval to Nathan Baker, the Secretary of War, he immediately responded 'For God's sake, don't tell the president about this or he'll stop the war!'" Morgan laughed. Earl couldn't help but join him.

Morgan looked out at the ocean and tried to imagine Earl's comparison to wheat fields on the Nebraska prairie. He didn't need any imagination though to feel his stomach churning as the ship rocked from the waves.

"Interesting isn't it?" Morgan said. "Saint-Nazaire was the first city we saw in France when we arrived—and now it's the last city in France we'll see as we head home."

He placed another pinch of Peachy Flanders in his mouth after realizing he had accidently swallowed the other wad when he laughed.

Earl's suitcase collection

Earl's suitcase collection

The army, being the army, decided to bring the troops back across the Atlantic in February. They traveled on the same ship that brought them to France—the USS *Mongolia*. Being on deck once again, Earl reflected back on how sick so many of them had been. They stayed on deck for as long as they could, wanting to be the first ones to spot the coast.

As Earl looked out on the horizon, a navy sailor approached him and said: "If you're hoping to spot the Jersey coast, private, you'll spot it in this direction," and pointed to the west.

"Thanks for the info. I'm real anxious to see the good ole U.S.A. again."

The two men shook hands.

"The name is Earl Young, from Nebraska."

"Glad to meet you, Earl. My name is Humphrey, from New York City. I've made this trip ferrying you doughboys back from France many times. So I know you'll be able to spot land in this direction in a couple of hours from now," Humphrey said.

"Care for a pinch of Big Chief?" Earl said, as he offered some to Humphrey.

"Well, thanks Earl. Big Chief, eh? That's my favorite chew but I've been out for a while." Humphrey stuck a clump of tobacco in his mouth. "I lost my bag of Big Chief a few months ago when the *Leviathan* was shelled by a German U boat."

"What happened?" Earl asked.

"We were just off the coast of Britain last summer. The fog was as thick as clam chowder. Three German U boats seemed to come out of nowhere. One of them got a lucky shot. The shell exploded close to where I was working. Some shrapnel hit me in the face. That's how I got this scar," Humphrey said, as he rubbed it with the back of his hand.

"I grew up on a farm and we used this salve called Bag Balm to help heal scars on our cows. Maybe some of that would help you," Earl said in an attempt to give some helpful advice.

"Guess it wouldn't hurt to try something like that but I think it's too late. The doctor on the ship—he should have stitched it up. I'd like to get some of that Bag Balm. I can think of some things I could do with it on that doctor," Humphrey said, relishing in the thought of a little revenge.

"I'll tell you what Humphrey. I don't have any Bag Balm on me but you can keep this bag of Big Chief. I can get some more soon because we are about to land." Earl handed the bag of chewing tobacco to him.

"Well thanks, Earl. This will certainly help as I've signed on to make a few more trips to help get you doughboys all back from France."

"I also told my friend, Morgan, that chewing Big Chief helped keep the Spanish flu from doin' me in."

Humphrey shook Earl's hand again and said, "In that case, I'll have some Big Chief every day so I won't get the flu. You keep a watch out for the coast. I've got to get back to work."

. . .

The USS *Mongolia* sailed into New York Harbor and docked at Hoboken, New Jersey. The army soldiers boarded ferryboats and went up the Hudson River a short distance to a military camp called Camp Merritt. The doughboys would stay at this camp for a few days while the army sorted out how to get them back to their home states. What a tremendous feeling to be back on U.S. soil. Earl felt like it had all been a dream.

Morgan won the first game of checkers, and Earl squeaked out a win in the second game. After Morgan made a triple jump to win the tiebreaker, Earl wrote a letter to the folks.

Pvt. Earl Young
Co. C. Casual B. N.
Merritt, New Jersey

Camp Merritt, N.J.
March 9, 1919

Dear Folks,
Well I suppose you have my telegram and was somewhat

Surprised? I can't realize it myself hardly. It most certainly seems just a wonderful day dream. This sailing across the ocean and riding in Real day coaches, sleeping on spring cots and eating pie, cake & ice cream once more. This camp sure is a nice one. Barracks all painted, cement roads and everything.

New York is just 11 miles southeast. Only costs $.85 to get over there either. I had a pass from noon Saturday till 8 a.m. Sunday morning. Several of us went over and deliberately took in the village. We saw lots of it from a truck roof. Never see one? A second story machine with wheels on each corner and a bunch of nuts on top. See? Well I guess we did see!

Saw a real show and an unusual comedy on 39 & Broadway. N.Y. is a nice place but I like Denver far better.

Lots to say but don't know just where to start so will hold it a week or two longer. Then both ends will meet better.

We move yet tonight to some casual company to be sent someplace else to be discharged. So possibly I will be in Kentucky, Texas, California or the lord only knows but figure to be home in a week or two! I don't know what my address is but it isn't 401 any more tho.

Will see you soon so go by,
Earl

They are just taking 2 of my buddies to the hospital for swelled jaws—mumps I guess. They can eat sour pickles tho.

This is Wed. night but will be going to Dodge, Iowa in a few days now.

Earl and a number of soldiers decided to see the sights in New City. Humphrey had given Earl the name of some good places for New York entertainment.

As they walked up and down Broadway, they were greeted like heroes, as a victorious army returning home to an enthusiastic welcome. Men in suits would stop to shake their hands. They were offered cigars and chocolates. Deli owners invited them in for free sandwiches. Women applauded. Beautiful ladies gave the boys a kiss on the cheek. Little children saluted the soldiers.

In the evening, Earl saw a Ziegfeld Follies show at the New Amsterdam Theatre. It was ironic that soldiers were enjoying a show inspired by the Follies Bergère of Paris. The women wore beautiful costumes and performed choreographed sets, and chorus girls dressed as battleships for a military salute—an outstanding performance. The stage was extravagant and no expense was spared to let the soldiers know how much they were appreciated.

23

Welcome Home

"Welcome Home"
Song lyrics by Bud Green, music by ED. Nelson; 1918

Skies of gray have given way to brightness.
Hearts that once were sad are feeling gay.
The news has flashed around,
Our boys are Homeward bound,
And we'll be there to meet them just to say:

Welcome home, the day of peace on earth is here.
Welcome home, what words of cheer.
We've kept our home fires a burning,
While yearning for you.
Your vacant chair is waiting, too;
You know you're welcome home.

Each mother's heart sings out with joy,
Welcome home my soldier boy.
And now that all the war clouds safely have past,
And God has brought me sunshine at last,
Oh welcome, welcome, you are welcome home.

Ev'ry mother's waiting for her loved one.
Ev'ry sweetheart's waiting at the pier.
Each baby will be glad,
To see her fighting Dad,
And this whole nation's proud to see you here.

It was obvious the nation was both overjoyed and relieved that the boys were home. Earl certainly enjoyed the Ziegfeld Follies and a vaudeville act that involved a juggling performance by W. C. Fields. He juggled cigar boxes at first. And then, as a tribute to the dough-boys, Fields juggled six army helmets. He was very entertaining and the soldiers stood and applauded during the act. Earl remembered a few of the funny quotes the actor made while juggling:

"The best cure for insomnia is to get a lot of sleep."

"Never try to impress a woman, because if you do she'll expect you to keep up the standard for the rest of your life."

"I never drink water because of the disgusting things that fish do in it."

Fields also performed a skit with billiards and some of the Ziegfeld Follies chorus girls. Earl laughed until he had tears in his eyes. He decided he would enjoy billiards and would look into it when he returned to Nebraska.

Earl and the doughboys marched up and down Broadway until five a.m. Just before he tumbled onto his cot, he wrote one last letter home before he mustered out of the military and ended his time as a soldier.

• • •

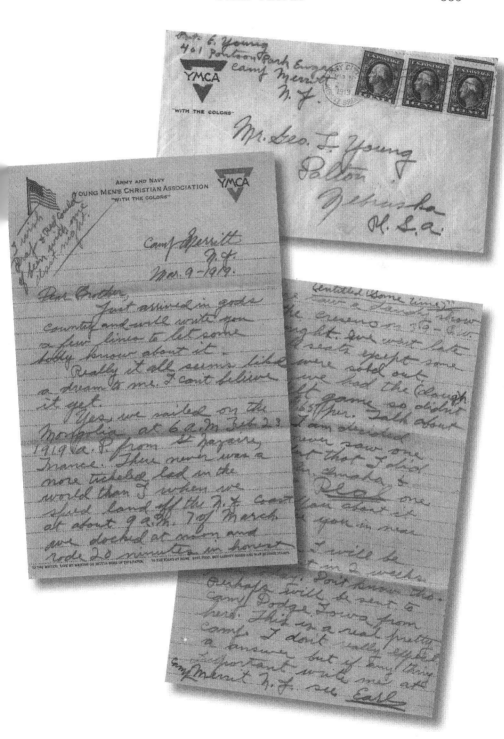

Pvt. Earl Young
401 Pontoon Park Engrs.
Camp Merritt, N.J.
Mar. 9, 1919

Dear Brother,

Just arrived in gods country and will write you a few lines to let somebody know about it. Really it all seems like a dream to me. I can't believe it yet.

Yes, we sailed on the Mongolia at 6 a.m. Feb 28, 1919 A.D. from St Nazaire, France. There never was a more tickled lad in the world than I when we spied land off the N.J. coast at about 9 a.m. 7 of March.

We docked at noon and rode 20 minutes in honest to god day coaches with plush cushions and everything. 20 min. more hike and we found ourselves in our barracks on hair mattresses and spring cots. We had to go through a delousing plant yet that night so didn't get to bed till 11 p.m. Made up for lost time tho later.

Sat. morning we again ("rolled packs") and moved 2 or 3 blocks more to other barracks at 3 p.m. Yesterday 43 of us put in for passes to New York City. Well we did promonade up & down Broadway to our hearts content until 5 a.m. this morning. We then caught a ferry across the river back to camp arriving here at 7:30 this morning.

I went to bed and never awoke until a while ago when they were having mail call & chicken dinner. A letter from Millie.

I sent a telegram home last night from Broadway.

Everybody gives the A.E.F. boys a glad hand and smiles that I enjoy but can't understand (& may be a bit stupid tho.) I like Denver better than New York. Although N.Y. is all there.

I am sitting in a Y.M.C.A. now waiting to see a show of some sort (entitled "Some Time"). I sure saw a dandy show at the Creseno on 39– B.W. last night. We went late and all seats except some boxes were sold out. Well we had the dough and felt game so didn't mind $1.65 per. Talk about shows. I am decided that I never saw one before, but that I did at Lincoln, Omaha & Denver. A REAL one. Will tell you about it when I see you in near future.

I figure I will be mustered out in 2 weeks from today. Don't know tho. Perhaps will be sent to Camp Dodge, Iowa from here. This is a real pretty camp. I don't really expect a answer but if anything important write me at Camp Merrit, N.J. See.

Earl
I wish Drap & Red could have been with me last night.

24

Tena

"How 'Ya Gonna Keep 'Em Down on the Farm
(After They've Seen Paree?)"
Song lyrics by Joe Young and Sam M. Lewis,
music by Walter Donaldson; 1919

"Rueben, Rueben, I've been thinking,"
Said his wifey dear;
"Now that all is peaceful and calm,
The boys will soon be back on the farm."
Mister Rueben started winking,
And slowly rubbed his chin.
He pulled his chair up close to mother,
And he asked her with a grin:

"How 'ya gonna keep 'em down on the farm,
After they've seen Paree?
How 'ya gonna keep 'em away from Broadway,
Jazzin' aroun' and paintin' the town?
How 'ya gonna keep 'em from harm?
That's a mystery.
They'll never want to see a rake or plow,
And who the deuce can parley-vous a cow?
How 'ya gonna keep 'em down on the farm,
After they've seen Paree?"

"Rueben, Rueben, you're mistaken,"
Said his wifey dear;
"Once a farmer, always a jay,
And farmers always stick to the hay."
"Mother Rueben, I'm not fakin'
Tho' you may think it strange,
But wine and women play the mischief,
With a boy who's loose with change."

"How 'ya gonna keep 'em down on the farm,
After they've seen Paree?
How 'ya gonna keep 'em away from Broadway,
Jazzin' aroun' and paintin' the town?
How 'ya gonna keep 'em from harm?
That's a mystery.
Imagine Rueben when he meets his pa.
He'll kiss his cheek and holler 'oo-la-la!'
How 'ya gonna keep 'em down on the farm,
After they've seen Paree?"

Time in France had gone by faster than time on the farm. No doubt about that. There were long days as a farmer. Long days plowing the fields. Long days disking the fields. Long days planting the wheat, then harvesting the wheat.

You worked. And you worked until everything was done. That's all there was to it.

And now, long days ahead would be eased with memories of his experiences and adventures in the army. By joining, he got to see much of the United States. The Statue of Liberty. A dogfight in France. He formed a bond with Morgan and would always remember the countless checker games and telling tall tales.

As buddies they'd complained about the army but wouldn't trade it for anything on account of how proud they were to be soldiers. They each determined the mettle of the other and held a quiet assurance they each had each other's back.

The Young family was filled with pride for their Earl. He was the only one of his brothers to have joined the army to fight the Kaiser. As a Jung or Young, he had become the family representative to defend their German heritage, giving him strength and character.

He did what needed to be done—just like on the farm, doing whatever was asked for the good of the situation at hand. He reflected on his disappointment when he first learned he wouldn't be a motorcycle dispatcher. But now, he considered himself very fortunate to have been in the 401stA.E.F. Engineers. What he learned there, he'd take into every new venture of his life. He knew he'd be a better farmer for it. In fact, he was planning someday to use an axle from a truck to build something special. Someday, it would be a large mower that he would design and build himself. There would come a day when Earl would read the letters he had mailed home and reflect on the experiences he may have even forgotten. Time would go by fast.

• • •

It was a hot, humid day in Nemaha County, Nebraska. It had been four months since Earl waved goodbye to the coast of France. It felt good to be back in Brock. It felt good to be working on his father's farm. No waiting for an order from an officer to get a drink. Freedom. He took a long drink of water from the well. The best water in the world. And he could say it was the best in the world as he had seen a lot of it.

He smiled at the thought of what he'd be doing that evening. There was a girl. Christene Keen. Her sisters called her Tena. Two days earlier, Earl summoned up the courage to ask Tena's father if he could take her out on a date. Her father agreed that Earl could take her to the movies in Talmage, but only as long as her sisters went with them. Earl didn't care. He just wanted to be with her and desperately hoped he could make a good impression.

He wiped the sweat from his face and took another long drink. There was more hay to load on the wagon before his date. And hay came first. Pushing a pitchfork into a stack of hay, Earl couldn't help but think how great it was to not have to wake up hearing the call of reveille. It's amazing what you quickly grow accustomed to.

The army was over. The war was over. The war of fighting the Kaiser. His own war fighting influenza. The war fighting frogs. And mud. All of it taught him how to fight against whatever the world would throw at him. He was proud to have been a soldier. He was proud to say he'd crossed the pond. Proud to have done all he could do to secure liberty and freedom for his family in Brock and in Dalton. He hoped this freedom would endure for his future generations.

MILITARY SERVICE

is essentially unselfish service. It implies personal hardship, discomfort, inconvenience, financial loss, broken health and many other forms of sacrifice even unto the giving of life itself. So America's soldiers, sailors, marines and nurses are most honored of all the people.

The State of Nebraska has inscribed upon its Roll of Honor the name of

Earl Young

May his service to the Nation in its hour of greatest trial serve to elicit the esteem of all patriotic citizens, and may his brilliant acts of devotion to Country serve as an everlasting inspiration to all loyal citizens of the Republic to place national welfare above individual selfishness, or personal gain.

In willing obedience to an act of the legislature at its last regular session, I, Samuel R. McKelvie, Governor of the State of Nebraska, do hereunto subscribe my name and have caused to be affixed the Great Seal of the State of Nebraska, this, the ___30th___ day of ___July___ 1921

By the Governor

Samuel R. McKelvie

Darius M. Amsberry
Secretary of State

H. J. Paul
Adjutant General

Earl's mother placed a bowl of deep red radishes on the kitchen table in front of Earl, then walked away to retrieve her German Bible, hidden behind the large flour sack. She opened it to Isaiah 2:4 and read how swords would be turned into plowshares again. She was proud to have a son who'd been part of the American Expeditionary Force but overjoyed that he was home again. Opening to the article she'd read that morning in the Auburn paper, she told Earl that this was to be the war to end all wars. She said a prayer that this would be so.

She could smile once again, watching Earl as he put salt on the radishes and eat them his favorite way—with the tails on. She would spoil him with pumpkin pie and homemade ice cream, and his father would convert all that food into energy to help on the farm. It all balanced out.

Walking out of the house through the wooden, screen door, Earl inhaled the wonderful aroma of cinnamon as it filled the kitchen. He wished he could grab the smell of the cinnamon rolls rising on the stove and stick it in his pocket. Then he could take out that aroma and breathe it in whenever he wanted.

Earl had accomplished what he set out to do. He had been part of something that required traveling half way around the world. He saw wonderful things that would give him a lifetime of memories. Civil War battlefields. The Virginia woods. Pontoon bridges. The Atlantic Ocean. Brave men—all ready to spit in the eyes of the Kaiser.

He fully understood the words in the song *America the Beautiful*. He had seen the purple mountain majesties. The amber waves of grain. The alabaster cities gleam. And most importantly, helped America continue to raise the banner of the free.

Now, he was free to think ahead about his future and wonder if something might develop after an evening at the movies with Tena. Would she be interested in an army soldier who wanted to be a farmer? Earl did have a few questions answered. He knew there was really only one place for him to live and what he wanted to do. He would be a farmer. He would grow wheat. Someday he would raise a family. Someday he would enjoy his grandchildren and great-grandchildren.

Nebraska.

Brock, Nebr.
Sat Eve., 7-26-19

Dear Bro,

 Received your letter the other day and was glad to hear from you folks. Sure am glad that you have a good wheat crop this year again. Our wheat did about 26 ½ Bu. per. Lots of straw this year and believe me it is heavy too. We got $1.54 for ours and costs $.85 to thresh. The spring wheat in this country is mostly weeds so it don't amount to much.

 Tell Gerald to say that wish he could have been here when we threshed, Donald too. They had a regular rig here anyway. A Russell Compound and 36 Rumley. Sure could eat the grain.

 I worked so blamed hard I made myself sick and haven't done a lick since Wed. Morn. Sure got my goat. (Am able to see Tena tomorrow tho I guess.) They only had three jobs to finish so I guess they get done tonight anyway. We had a full crew all the way through. Say, what kind of machinery have you got and how much of it anyway how does it all run?

Dad said the other night when we told him you had good wheat that this darned land here ain't worth no $400 per according to Cheyenne. I suppose you had better look for a location for some land there. Anyhow a couple of weeks after I get the wheat sowed if the Chalmers is still running. Sure is some car.

How are Jul & Ed getting along. Don't let Julius get acquainted with no cook out there. Does Ed still go to Bridgeport.

Say, what became of Paul Draper Jr. I haven't heard of him since I got home. Harry Scott either. Did Blackwell & Baumbach get out of the army yet? Say, that saddle arrived in fine shape. But where the duce is that bridle to match.

Hot winds today. Need rain bad. Corn is good yet. Sun went down hazey tonight. 7:15 now. Tena will soon be waiting.

So Goodbye and Ans. Soon.

Earl
(Ma sent some beads today. Hope you get them all O.K.)

Wedding of Earl Young and Christena (Tena) Keen, May 4, 1921. Earl, standing on right. Christena, sitting; Lena Keen, bridesmaid; and Harvey Thompson, best man.

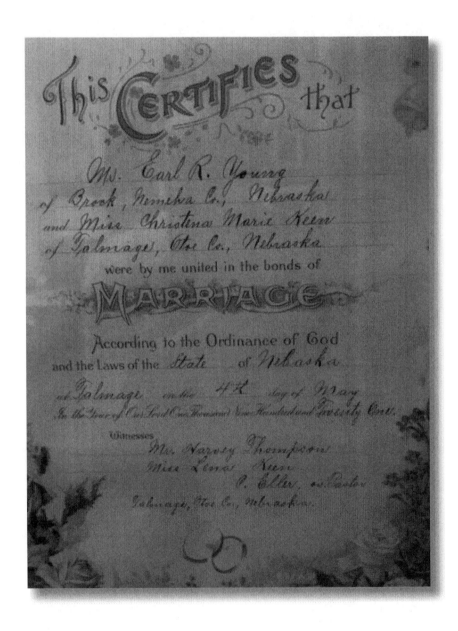

Acknowledgments

Thank you Margaret for being there at the very beginning. You started my journey to write a book by asking the question, "What's inside that dusty suitcase?"—and then helping me determine what to do with our discovery.

Thank you Mindy, Todd, and Tammy at Feathered Horse Publishing. Your advice, guidance, and long hours of editing helped make this book possible. You helped me finish the journey by taking as much interest in my family history as I did. You could say that I became your number one fan.

Historical Background

The following historical background begins with notes on cities of Nebraska and ends with notes on Earl and Christene Young; notes in between are alphabetically placed.

Brock, Nebraska

Brock, Nebraska, is "known as the town of many names." It was founded in 1854 as Shroaf's Ford. The name was changed to Bradley's Bridge in 1855, Dayton in 1856, Howard in 1867, Clinton in 1880, Podunk in 1880 and then Brock in 1882. It is in eastern Nebraska, in Nemaha County. The first school, known as Old Union, opened in 1884 as a country school, a half-mile west of town. The population of Brock peaked in 1900 with 543 residents and at that time had an opera house, movie theatre, dance hall, and a number of stores. (brocknebraska.weebly.com; casde.unl.edu/history/counties/nemaha/brock)

Dalton, Nebraska

Dalton, Nebraska, is in the western part of the state, in Cheyenne County. The population in 1918 was 289. A newspaper ad in 1908 described Dalton as "land that is level, having a rich black soil five feet deep with a clay subsoil underneath. There never was a better chance for men to get close to a good town and have better soil than this." (www.casde.unl.edu/history/counties/cheyenne/dalton)

Cheyenne County, Nebraska

The county is rectangular in form, about 100 miles by 50 miles in size, or 5,100 square miles, or 3,264,000 acres. In 1909 only 15,479 acres of wheat were planted, 14,403 acres of corn planted, and 28,005 acres of hay—which means, a lot of native grass had not yet been farmed, and still open range for ranching. The census taken in 1910 listed a population of 4,551 for the entire county of which 45 percent of the population had a German ancestry. (*History of the State of Nebraska* by William Cutler. Chicago: Western Historical Company, A. T., 1882; and http://www.usgen-net.org/usa/ne/topic/resources/andreas/hon_cnty.htm)

Potter, Nebraska

Potter, Nebraska, is located in Cheyenne County. Farmers in this area grew mostly wheat and oats in the early 1900s. The town had a large number of businesses, considering its small size, with a population of 232 in the 1910 census. By 1915 Potter had a brick schoolhouse, general stores, grocery stores, banks, churches, and the Potter Drug Company—the pharmacist was James Earl Thayer, who also operated a sundry where you could find sodas, candy, stationary, magazines, and ice cream. *The Potter Review*, the local newspaper, called it "the biggest little city in Nebraska." (www.casde.unl.edu/history/counties/cheyenne/potter)

•   •   •

Army Corps of Engineers

The Advanced Services of the A.E.F. was created to provide the infrastructure to win the war. Army engineers built floating and fixed bridges across rivers, constructed railways for trains, roads, port facilities, buildings, and hospitals, dug trenches, cut trees for lumber, placed and dismantled barbed wire, and maintained telephones and signaling equipment.

The Advanced Services in WWI had a distinctive insignia, with a large center Cross of Lorraine and the letters A and S on either side of the cross, surrounded by a blue circle. The Cross of Lorraine was a symbol of the defense for a free France. The shoulder patch was worn by a wide variety of support units composed of Engineer, Quartermaster, Medical, Signal Corps, and Ordnance units with soldiers trained for specific functions. (The *Doughboys: The Story of the A.E.F, 1917 – 1918* by Laurence Stallings. Popular Library, 1964)

Army Training Camps WWI

The U.S. Army constructed 32 training camps where civilians became soldiers. The construction began in June of 1917 and, by November 1918, four million soldiers were trained. Some received specialized training in new areas of military involvement. The army had a number of airfields all across the U.S. to train pilots such as Camp Funston in San Antonio that provided a two-month basic course for pilots. Camp Holt provided training for a new piece of military equipment—the tank. Their training exercises took place on the Civil War battlefield at Gettysburg, Pennsylvania. Their commanding officer was a captain taking charge of his first command—Dwight D. Eisenhower. (*The First World War: A Photographic History* by Laurence Stallings. Simon & Schuster, 1933.)

Camel Cigarettes

The R.J. Reynolds Company in North Carolina introduced Camel cigarettes in 1913. The company introduced innovative advertising to America with promotions proclaiming, "The Camels Are Coming." Circus camels were paraded in towns, and a package of Camels sold for a nickel when other companies sold their tobacco cigarettes for ten cents. Camels were a revolutionary product, as they were made with burley, a thin leafed, light color, American tobacco blended with Turkish tobacco. This combination produced a different and popular tasting cigarette.

"Say Earl, did you try one of those new cigarettes that the chorus girls passed out last night?" Morgan asked.

"The ones named Camels? Those were strange. Each cigarette was already rolled when you took it out of the package. I don't think they'll be very popular. It's just as easy to roll your own. It's amazing to me the things that people come up with," Earl said.

Camp Merritt

There were many army training camps spread across the States from coast to coast. Camp Merritt was unique because it was quite often the last stop to prepare soldiers for their overseas journey. The camp was located 10 miles south of New York City in Hoboken, New Jersey. Camp Merritt was over 700 acres in size, and over two million soldiers departed from this site to cross the pond. Over 75 percent of the troops sent to France embarked on ships from Hoboken. A rallying cheer of the A.E.F. became "Heaven, Hell, or Hoboken." (*America and World War I: A Traveler's Guide* by Mark D. Van Ells. Interlink Pub Group, 2014.)

Flanders Field

Flanders is a plateau region in the north half of Belgium. In May of 1915 Lieutenant John McCrae (1872–1918), a Canadian soldier, wrote a poem to honor a close friend who was killed during the Battle of Ypres in Belgium.

"In Flanders Fields"

In Flanders fields the poppies blow
Between the crosses, row on row
That mark our place, and in the sky,
The larks, still bravely singing, fly,
Scarce heard amid the guns below.

We are the dead. Short days ago
We lived, felt dawn, saw sunset glow,
Loved and were loved, and now we lie
In Flanders fields.

Take up our quarrel with the foe:
To you from failing hands we throw
The torch; be yours to hold it high.
If ye break faith with us who die,
We shall not sleep, though poppies grow
In Flanders fields.

There is a cemetery in Waregem, Belgium, named Flanders Field American Cemetery to honor 367 doughboys who died while fighting in Belgium. The name is derived from the poem. In the center of the cemetery is a limestone chapel. Above the chapel door are the words "Greet them ever with grateful hearts." (http://www. flandersfieldsmusic.com/thepoem.html. https://www.nps.gov/hdp/ exhibits/abmc/flanders_index.htm)

General John J. Pershing

General Pershing, commander of the American Expeditionary Forces, initially only had 200,000 men in the army when the U.S. declared war on Germany. His philosophy was to not send troops to France until they were trained and ready. He also insisted that his army, when they were ready, would fight only under American commanders and not as replacement soldiers in Britain's troops.

"Black Jack" Pershing was an officer in the African-American 10th Cavalry Regiment, where he earned his nickname during the Indian Wars with battles against Geronimo and the Apaches in the Southwest. In 1891 he was a military science instructor and earned a law degree at the University of Nebraska. He commanded his black troopers in the Battle of San Juan in 1898 with Teddy Roosevelt's Roughriders. He married the daughter of the senator who chaired the Military Affairs Committee, was a friend of President Roosevelt and, with these contacts, promoted from captain to general in 1906.

Pershing was not in favor of the armistice with Germany, instead wanting an unconditional surrender with occupation of Germany to permanently destroy German militarism. Pershing is the only American to be promoted in his own lifetime to General of the Armies, the highest possible rank in the United States Army. The rank has only been held twice in American history, an honor awarded posthumously to George Washington. (*World War I: The Definitive Visual History* by R.G. Grant. DK Publishing 2014; and *Encyclopedia Britannica*)

German Submarines

Germany disregarded international law that protected neutral nations' ships and declared in February 1915 they would sink any ship without warning, even a merchant ship. The Unterseeboot, or U-boat, was used effectively by Germany to sink unsuspecting Allied vessels. The *William P. Frye*, an American merchant vessel, transporting grain to England, was sunk in March 1915. In May 1915 New York newspapers published a warning by the German embassy that Americans traveling on ships in war zones did so at their own risk.

The *Lusitania*, a British passenger ship, was sunk on May 7, 1915, killing over 1,000 people, including 128 Americans. The U.S. demanded an end to German attacks on unarmed passenger and merchant ships, to which Germany pledged. In November 1915 an Italian ocean liner was sunk without warning, killing 27 Americans. Public opinion in the U.S. began to turn against Germany. Determined to win the war, Germany announced in January 1917 the resumption of unrestricted warfare. The United States then severed diplomatic relations with Germany. U.S. Congress passed an arms bill to ready the nation for war in February 1917. Germany sank four more U.S. merchant ships in March 1917. In April 1917 a declaration of war against Germany was issued by U.S. Congress. Germany sank over 5,000 ships during WWI. (*America's War for Humanity: Pictorial History of the World War for Humanity* by Thomas H. Russell. L. H. Walter 1919; and *Horrors and Atrocities of the Great War, Including the Tragic Destruction of the Lusitania* by Logan Marshall. Universal Book and Bible House 1915.)

Influenza Vaccinations

The world is arguably as vulnerable to another flu pandemic as it was in 1918, even though flu vaccinations are available now. The 1918 flu strain originated as an avian flu that mutated into a form that infected humans. Genetic mutations are possible for an influenza virus to cause a deadly pandemic again. Unlike other vaccinations, flu vaccinations are necessary every year because the virus mutates from one year to the next. It's evolution at work—mutations help the virus evade detection by the human immune system. It is also possible for a flu virus to become especially virulent and cause a superinfection. This then causes a pandemic because the population doesn't have any immunity and the virus quickly spreads.

The Nebraska Council of Defense in 1917

The Council initially coordinated the production and conservation of food, the supply of farm labor, and organized Liberty Loan drives. It evolved into a police presence to monitor the loyalty and attitudes of Nebraska citizens, especially those of German heritage. If a citizen was determined questionable, they were "dealt with by the Council in a manner suited to the circumstances." People who spoke German or who were otherwise questionable were threatened with inquisition panels, written summons, and imprisonment. Men of German birth were instructed to be even more careful than any other in his conversation and conduct.

A sign was placed at the post office in Avoca, Nebraska, that read: "No German talk in this town or there will be tar and feathers."

William Harding, a Sioux City lawyer and Iowa governor, issued a statement making it illegal to use any language but English in public. He said in a public speech that God did not hear prayers spoken in any language but English. "While fighting to make the world safe for democracy, Nebraskans nearly lost it at home." (https://history.nebraska.gov. https://www.omaha.com; see article entitled: "During World War I Nebraska and Iowa Nearly Lost Sight of Democracy"; and (Nebraska: A Pictorial History by Bruce Nicollo. University of Nebraska Press, 1967.)

"Old Montana" Poem

This poem comes from an author-owned postcard with an illustration of a cowboy in buckskins (perhaps The Virginian) saying, "Smile, damn you!" alongside the poem "Old Montana," what appears to be a version of J. Campbell Cory's poem "Old Montana." The postcard is split back, used, and postmarked "Billings 1909," and mailed to Harvard, Illinois. Inked note reads as follows:

Billings Mont. 11/16 -09

Dear Mother, just received your letter O.K. and glad to hear from you. Going up towards Butte from here tonight. Business is good.

Kindest regards to all,

Ed.

Pancho Villa

Mexico was in revolution in 1916, and Germany tried to convince Mexico to form an alliance to strike the United States. Germany promised they would help Mexico get back the states that were lost to them in the Mexican-American War of 1847: New Mexico, Arizona, California, and Texas. A band of Mexican rebels under the command of Pancho Villa raided Columbus, New Mexico, in March of 1916. The raid escalated into a battle when soldiers from a nearby army camp drove Villa back into Mexico. Eight U.S. soldiers died in the battle. President Woodrow Wilson ordered an expedition into Mexico to capture Pancho Villa. It was led by

General John J. Pershing. Villa was never captured but this event is one that led to Pershing's appointment as commander of the A.E.F.

Roscoe "Dusty" Rhodes

Roscoe Rhodes from Ansley, Nebraska, was the captain-elect of the 1918 Nebraska Cornhusker football team. He enlisted in the army and was placed in a division that was sent to France within one month of enlistment. Roscoe was killed in action in France in October 1918. He became an inspiration for the Memorial Stadium name.

The Siman Act

World War One produced an extensive campaign against all things German, from the performance of German music at concerts, speaking German in schools and giving sermons in German or singing German hymns in church services. In October of 1918, the Nebraska legislature introduced a bill, named the Siman Act, and it was enacted in the spring of 1919. It provided that "No person, individually or as a teacher, shall, in any private, denominational, parochial or public school, teach any subject to any person in any language other than the English language."

In May of 1920, the Siman Act was used to convict a teacher, Robert Meyer, of a one-room schoolhouse in Hampton, Nebraska, of reading to a fourth-grade boy in German.

The Nebraska Supreme Court affirmed his conviction, citing it as a proper response to "the baneful effects" of allowing immigrants to educate their children in German, with results "inimical to our own safety."

The case went to the Supreme Court of the United States. They ruled in favor of Robert Meyer, stating that "an individual has certain fundamental rights which must be respected. Mere knowledge of the German language cannot reasonably be regarded as harmful. The protection of the Constitution extends to all, to those who speak other languages as well as to those born with the English language." (*Nebraska: A Pictorial History* by Bruce Nicollo. University of Nebraska Press, 1967.)

Smokes for Soldiers and Sailors

"Smokes for Soldiers and Sailors" was a tobacco fund established by Lord Kitchener in 1914. 'Smoke Clouds' was a card series produced by Bamforths & Co. of Homfirth, England. It was just one of many funds established that used advertising for their products on cigarette packs and postcards. Cheap cigarettes were soon as much a part of army life as trenches and barbed wire. (https://www.worldwar1postcards.com/the-story-behind-a-ww1-postcard.php)

Spanish Influenza

The influenza pandemic of 1918 to 1919 infected one-third of the entire world population and killed an estimated 59 million people. It was known as the Spanish Flu or La Grippe. More than 25 percent of the U.S. population became sick and 675,000 died, ten times as many as in the First World War. Many flu victims were young, otherwise healthy adults and 43,000 servicemen died. Spanish Influenza is a virus that attacks the respiratory system, causing pneumonia. It was highly contagious and physicians were helpless to treat patients as they struggled to clear their airways to not suffocate. As the pneumonia progressed to cyanosis, patients would turn blue from lack of oxygen and die, often within hours of contracting the disease. (https://news.nationalgeographic.com/news/2014/01/140123-spanish-flu-1918-china-origins-pandemic-science-health/. https://virus.stanford.edu/uda/. http://time.com/5116388/flu-pandemic-1918/)

Spy Intrigue

A secret diplomatic communication from Germany to Mexico was intercepted by British intelligence and turned over to President Wilson. The message was from Arthur Zimmermann, the German foreign secretary, and proposed that Mexico form an alliance with Germany against the U.S. In return for their help, Germany would help Mexico recover the territory it lost to the U.S. in the 1840s, including Texas, New Mexico, Arizona, and California. The note was published on the front page of newspapers across the entire U.S. and propelled U.S. sentiment to declare war against Germany. (*World War I: How the Great War Made the Modern World*. The Atlantic Books, July 2014.)

Tootsie Roll

Leo Hirshfield, an Austrian immigrant, worked at a candy shop in New York City, owned by Stern & Staalberg. He worked to perfect a chocolate tasting hard candy that would not melt in the heat and named his candy "Tootsie Roll," after his daughter Clara "Tootsie" Hirshfield. The Tootsie Roll became the fist individually wrapped candy, and the company name was changed to The Sweets Company of America in 1917. The company also produced a popular candy ad-vertised as a "healing blend of sugar, honey, horehound, and menthol" named the "Lance Cough Drop." Their motto was "cut the cough."

Trench Cake

The 1916 trench cake recipe is from Elizabeth Craig's book *Elizabeth Craig's Economical Cookery*. Restrictions during the war were necessary, and the cake contained no eggs and more cocoa powder to add a bit of luxury to a fruitcake destined for the boys who served in WWI. (*Elizabeth Craig's Economical Cookery*. Collins, 1950.)

Two Fields of Honor

The farmer and the soldier both brought victory in WWI. American farmers increased their production to support soldiers in U.S. training camps and overseas. The food produced helped civilians and military maintain physical strength, and morale and commitment to the war effort. Additionally, American farmers supplied Allies with meat and grain. Britain imported 80 percent of their wheat and 60 percent of their total food supply from the U.S. The two fields of honor were the wheat fields and battlefields. Whether they served on the "Home Front" or "Over There," Nebraskans and other Americans played an important role for victory and established the United States as a world power. (*One Hundred War Cartoons* by Villeneuve, 1918. The cartoon sketch, "Two Fields of Honor," and the other cartoons used in the book, come from Villeneuve's collection in *One Hundred War Cartoons*; the cartoonist was George Colburn. Cartoons were printed in the *Idaho Daily Statesman,* starting in 1914, and continuing during WWI. The author-owned book was purchased at an antique store in 2013. On the book is a stamp that reads Carnegie Public Library, Boise, Idaho.) (*The Nebraska Story* by George E. Condra, James Olson, and Royce Knapp. Illustrated by Terry Townsend and Stanley Sohl. Lincoln: The University Publishing Co., 1951.)

The Vaterland

The *Vaterland* was a German ocean liner used for transatlantic ocean service. The English translation is fatherland, meaning native country. The ship was docked stateside when the United States entered the war. The *Vaterland* was seized by the U.S. government and converted to a troopship able to carry over 21,000 soldiers. (*World War I: The Definitive Visual History* by R.G. Grant. DK Publishing, 2014.)

Volunteer Training Corps

The Volunteer Training Corps originated in Britain in 1914 and was also formed in America, where it was nicknamed "The Home Guards." It was organized for men "too old" for military service—men who could not pass a physical for military duty or men who were older and could volunteer to join. It was originally known as the Volunteer Training Corps, or VTC, formed for public safety and to protect civilian lives. They had uniforms and also provided honor guards at funerals, sold liberty bonds, and supported the Red Cross. Unfortunately, there were those who said the VTC initials stood for "Volumes of Tired Old Crabs."

W. C. Fields

W. C. Fields started his career in vaudeville and later performed with the Ziegfield Follies in New York City from 1915 to 1921. Some called him "the world's greatest juggler." He was a comedian with many memorable quotes:

"I cook with wine, sometimes I even add it to the food."

"Start every day with a smile and get it over with."

"The world is getting to be such a dangerous place,
a man is lucky to get out of it alive."

(https://www.brainyquote.com/authors/w_c_fields)

WWI Battles

Somme: the first day of battle began on July 1,1914, and British troops endured 60,000 casualties on that day alone. The battle lasted over four months, more than one million men were killed or wounded, and Allied troops gained seven miles.

Meuse-Argonne: American troops attacked German positions on October 11, 1918. The battle lasted 47 days, involved 1.2 million American troops, more than any other clash in history. American casualties in this battle numbered 26,277. The battle ended with the armistice, on November 11, 1918.

Belleau-Wood: the United States fought their first battle of WWI in May 1918. Fighting was ferocious, with hand to hand combat. Battle tested French troops advised a tactical withdrawal. Marine Captain Lloyd Williams responded, "Retreat? Hell, we just got here!" The U.S. troops had fighting spirit but their shortage of combat experience was evident when they advanced in dense waves over open wheat fields. They suffered over 1,000 casualties on their first day of battle. Fighting continued for three weeks and the German advance to overtake Paris was stopped. By July 1918 the size of the A.E.F. in France increased to over one million men. Any serious possibility of Germany winning the war had evaporated. (*America and World War I: A Traveler's Guide* by Mark D. Van Ells. Interlink Pub Group, 2014; *Collier's New Photographic History of the World's War* by Francis J. Reynolds and C. W. Taylor. New York: P. F. Collier & Sons, 1919; *World War I: How the Great War Made the Modern World.* The Atlantic Books, July 2014; *World War I: The Definitive Visual History* by R.G. Grant. DK Publishing, 2014)

• • •

Earl and Christene Young

Earl Young was born May 2, 1899, in Brock, Nebraska. His parents were Joseph Young and Elizabeth Marie Schmelzel Young. Joseph Young's father was Fredrick Jung who came to Nebraska from Illinois and changed the family name from Jung to Young. Elizabeth Schmelzel Young's parents were Fredrick Schmelzel, born in 1833 in Baiern, Germany, and Gertrude Brittlle Schmelzel, born in 1825 at Rheim Preussen, Germany. They emigrated from Germany to Riken, Illinois, and were married in 1859.

Christene Marie Keen was born on June 29, 1900, in Talmage, Nebraska. Her parents were Fredrick Keen and Cathrine Skrdla Keen. Fredrick Keen's parents were Fredrick and Roseanna Kuehn, who emigrated to Wisconsin from Germany and changed their German name from Kuehn to Keen. Catherine Skrdla emigrated from Austria; her father was Joseph Skrdla.

Earl R. Young of Brock, Nemaha County, Nebraska, and Christene Marie Keen of Talmage, Otoe County, Nebraska, were united in the bonds of marriage on May 4, 1921.

Family lore supposedly says that Earl was not given a middle name when he was born and even though he could enlist in the army without a middle name, he couldn't marry without a middle name. The family does not have an explanation of why R was chosen or what the R stands for—it must have just sounded good at the time.

Bibliography

Baring-Gould, Sabine. *Now the Day is Over*. *The Church Times*, February 16, 1867.

Berlin, Irving. *Good-bye France (You'll Never Be Forgotten by the U.S.A.)*. New York: Waterson, Berlin & Snyder Co., 1918. Sheet Music.

Berlin, Irving. *Oh! How I Hate to Get Up in the Morning!* New York: Waterson, Berlin & Snyder Co., 1918. Sheet Music.

Berlin, Irving. *They Were All Out of Step but Jim*. New York: Waterson, Berlin & Snyder Co., 1918. Sheet Music.

Birks, H. Fred. "The Cowboy's Farewell to the Dryland Farmer."

Bryan, Alfred and Joe McCarthy. Composed by Fred Fisher. *Wee, Wee, Marie*. New York: McCarthy & Fisher, 1918. Sheet Music.

Bryan, Alfred. Composed by Harry Tierney. *It's Time for Every Boy to be a Soldier*. Detroit: Jerome H. Remick & Co., 1917. Sheet Music.

Buchanan, D. M. Composed by Ned Clay. *We're on Our Way to France to Fight for Liberty*. Indianapolis: Seidel Music Publishing Co., 1917. Sheet Music.

Carr, "Kid" Howard, Harry Russell, and Jimmie Havens. *We Don't Want the Bacon: What We Want Is a Piece of the Rhine*. Chicago: Arcade Music Pub. Co., 1918. Sheet Music.

Collins, Dean. Composed by Lyn Udall. *My Red Cross Girl Goodbye*. Portland: J. H. Keating Co., 1914. Sheet Music.

Dempsey, J. E. Composed by Joseph A. Burke. *A Soldier's Rosary*. New York: A. J. Stasny Music Co., 1918. Sheet Music.

Fields, Arthur. Composed by Leon Flatow. *It's a Long Way to Berlin but We'll Get There*. New York: Leo, Feist, Inc., 1917. Sheet Music.

Ford, Lena Guilbert. Composed by Ivor Novello. *Keep the Home Fires Burning(' Till the Boys Come Home)*. New York: Chappell & Co. Ltd., 1915. Sheet Music.

Gilbert, L. Wolfe, Malvin Franklin, and Anatol Friedland. Composed by L. Wolfe Guilbert. *Set Aside Your Tears (Till the Boys Come Marching Home)*.New York: Jos. W. Stern & Co., 1917. Sheet Music.

Goodwin, Joe and Ballard MacDonald. Composed by James F. Hanley. *Three Wonderful Letters from Home*. New York: Shapiro, Bernstein & Co., 1918. Sheet Music.

Green, Bud. Composed by Ed. G. Nelson. *Welcome Home*. New York: A.J. Stasny Music Co., 1918. Sheet Music.

Halpine, Charles G. *The Life and Adventures, Songs, Services, and Speeches of Private Miles O'Reilly: (47th Regiment, New York, Volunteers)*. New York: Carleton, 1864. 178-79. Print.

Johnson, Philander. Music by Joseph E. Howard. Arranged by Harry W. Howard. *Somewhere in France Is the Lily*. New York: M. Witmark & Sons, 1917. Sheet Music.

Lewis, Sam M. and Joe Young. Composed by M.K. Jerome. *Just a Baby's Prayer at Twilight for Her Daddy Over There*. New York: Waterson Berlin & Snyder Co., 1918. Sheet Music.

Lewis, Sam M. and Joe Young. Composed by Walter Donaldson. *How 'Ya Gonna Keep 'Em Down on the Farm (After They've Seen Paree?)*. New York: Waterson, Bernstein & Snyder, 1919. Sheet Music.

Luther, Martin. *Ein feste Burg ist unser Gott*. Germany: 1529. Translated in English by Frederick Hedge: *A Mighty Fortress Is Our God*. 1852. Hymn.

Luther, Martin. *Von Himmel hoch, da komm' ich her*. Germany: 1535. Translated in English by Cahterine Winkworth: *From Heaven Above to Earth I Come*. 1855. Hymn.

Mahoney, Jack. Composed by Halsey K. Mohr. *The Statue of Liberty Is Smiling: On the Hearts of the World To-day*. New York: Shapiro, Bernstein & Co., 1918. Sheet Music.

"Old Montana." Version of poem "Old Montana" by J. Campbell Cory. Butte: Cohn Brothers, circa 1909.

"Our Boys Need Sox—Knit Your Bit American Red Cross." New York: American Lithographic Co., [between 1914 and 1918]. Poster.

Root, George F. *Just Before the Battle, Mother*. Chicago: Root & Cady, 1863. Sheet Music.

Sterling, Andrew B. Composed by Arthur Lange. *A Mother's Prayer for Her Boy Out There*. New York: Joe Morris Music Co., 1918. Sheet Music.

Villeneuve. *One Hundred War Cartoons*. n.p. (See "Notes" for description.)

Sterling, Andrew B., Bernie Grossman, and Arthur Lange. Composed by Arthur Lange. *We're Going Over*. New York: Joe Morris Music Co., 1917. Sheet Music.

Sterling, Andrew. Composed by Arthur Lange. *America, Here's My Boy*. New York: Joe Morris Music Co., 1917. Sheet Music.

Whiting, Olive. *Khaki Knitting Book*. New York: Allies Special Aid, 1917.

Whitson, Beth Slater. Composed by Harry I. Robinson. *In the Garden of Memory*. Chicago: Will Rossiter, 1912. Sheet Music.

Wilbur, Lawrence. "American Red Cross Serves Humanity." New York: Snyder & Black, Inc., 1914. Poster.

Williams, Harry and Jack Judge. *It's a Long, Long Way to Tipperary*. New York: *Chappell & Co., Ltd.,* 1912. Sheet Music.

Wood, Will. *American Crusaders March*. New York: Will Wood, 1918. Sheet Music.

Young, Earl. To the Young family. *Personal Letters*. In author's possession.

Young, Joe and Sam Lewis. Composed by Bert Grant. *The Tale the Church Bell Told: Someone Will Answer for My Silence*. New York: Waterson-Berlin & Snyder, 1918. Sheet Music.